D1029176

THE RED STRANGER

THE
RED STRANGER

DAVID STEPHEN

Illustrated by Maurice Wilson

LUTTERWORTH PRESS
LONDON

For
Alistair, Jimmy and Sidney
Editors and good friends
over many years

Contents

The Grand Duc came for Christmas

IT was one of the worst storms the moor folk could remember.

Old Tulloch at the loch cottage—lean, garrulous and seventy—had never known anything like it. He had seen giant trees felled by the storms of many winters. He had seen snow drifted to eave height, and three Greenland falcons tossed down on the moor in a blizzard of Arctic fury. Yet he would have told you it was the worst blow within memory.

For two days, now east, now north-east, the wind raked the moor with its icy talons and howled like a wolf-pack down the cottage chimneys. It tipped feeding birds under the tail till they danced in unwilling circles, and swept Smokey Joe, the old hoodie crow, from the pine roost where he rocked flat-footed in sleep. In Glencryan Wood the serried spruces fell in swathes.

The loch froze, and the brimmed ditches ran silent under glass-ice veined with white. Then the snow came, and the world was a swirling chaos. The wild geese fled from the loch;

waxwings gathered in the bushes beside the cottage on the shore. Old Tulloch, reading the signs, put on a heavy quilted jacket and said: "If this blaw lasts we'll ha'e Polar bears doon for Christmas an' Eskimos chappin' at the door gin Ne'erday."

At nightfall on the third day of the storm the snow was lying hedge-deep in the hollows; spruce, yew and pine were draped in ostrich plumes of startling whiteness. By moonrise, when the wind was coming from the east like liquid glass, the plumes were ice-crusted, with every twig encased in rime like the fur of ermines.

The wind fell suddenly. The moon rose clear in a dead calm, flooding the snowy vasts with blue-white radiance. In the clear, freezing sky the stars flickered with spectral blue and amethyst flame. To the south, Orion the Hunter strode glittering from the murk, travelling his immemorial sky-trail with the green-and-crimson-eyed Dog star at heel.

These were the moments of The Great Silence, when the moon floats, and the stars flicker, and the snow lies unmarked in ridges and furrows and escarpments, sculpted by the wind, the silence that follows a storm of Polar fury. Then, faintly, from the perimeter of the silence, came the yapping of a dog . . . the whistle of a locomotive. . . . Nearer, the bark of a fox. Then an owl hooting in Glencryan, and the rent fabric of the night was restored.

Out of the east, when the moon was at its height, came a great, dark bird, with the seeming bulk of an eagle, flying in tired moth flight about twenty feet above his own wavering ground shadow. Ducks *querked* in alarm when the dread shape passed overhead, but the newcomer flapped on to the pine strip reaching down to the shore and swept up into the first dark, shaggy-headed tree.

For a moment he sat in a shaft in revealing moonlight, which projected his enormous shadow on to the snow and betrayed him as an owl—an owl with great flaming eyes—an eagle owl from some far northern forest; the Grand Duc of the French and the most savagely powerful of the clan, a bird nearly three feet in length, who feared nothing that walked or crawled or flew.

No man can say why, or whence, he came; but it is likely he

came unwillingly, without any foreknowledge of his destination. Probably the same storm that felled the Glencryan spruces swept him up and out across the North Sea, buffeting and driving him inexorably towards a Scottish landfall. Certainly, he came in from the direction of Stirling, to find the moor when the wind was backing and pitch in a loch-side pine when its fury was spent.

The Grand Duc side-stepped along his perch till he was out of the glare of the moon. He drew himself up long, half closing his eyes, and erected his ear tufts. His fight with the blizzard had brought weariness more commanding than hunger and he wanted to sleep.

So he slept, where once the clansmen foraged and the skirling challenge of the great Highland War Pipes is now a faint, unheeded echo from the proud, unheeded past, while the moon's magic raised phantoms in philibegs and the iron entered the snow. And perhaps he dreamed—of primeval forests, scarred and brooding, where the elk still roams, of Teutonic woods where Goering hunted the boar and dreamed of conquest, of Baltic fastnesses, or Tannenberg, or forests that were once part of the empire of the Tsars.

Who knows? But his dreams, if he had any, were interrupted at half-past six in the morning by the barking of a terrier and the crunch of boots on frozen snow.

Jock Simpson, the fencer, had left home early that morning, with a bushman's saw over his shoulder and his terrier, Corrie, at heel. Because of the snow, he could not use his bicycle, and he knew he would be breaking the first trail to Firknowe Farm and the going would be heavy. He was wearing a tweed two-snooter, rubber boots, and Army gaiters laced down to keep out the snow.

Though daylight was yet a long way off, the white snow and the clear sky made all things plain, and Jock plodded along the moor road with his eyes on the yowdendrift ahead, looking for the first tracks of furtive feet. But the snow was untracked all the way to the loch. Jock was muttering to himself something about "beasts hae mair sense than bodies" when he was pulled up in his tracks by a strange, outlandish cry.

Kveck-kveck!

Corrie, scampering ahead over the frozen drifts, pricked his ears and barked. Jock called the dog to heel. He was frankly puzzled. He knew he was hearing something he had never heard before; but, shrewd in his judgement, he thought at once of some kind of owl.

While Jock stood listening and looking the Grand Duc glared from cover, with eyes bright and flaming as a leopard's. He had no fear of the man, and in the boot-high terrier he saw not a dangerous dog, but potential prey. Stretching himself, till his feathers were clear of his tremendous talons, he again uttered his wild, strange, menacing cry.

Kveck-kveck!

Corrie, a-quiver beside his master, rushed forward when he heard the cry, and at the same moment the Grand Duc launched himself at the dog. As the great owl swooped Corrie turned, with tail down, yelping. He was a big-hearted little dog, used for going to ground after foxes, but when he saw the great owl sailing in at roe height his courage melted and he bolted towards his master.

Jock Simpson had seen more than most men of the dramas of the woods, but the appearance of the Grand Duc almost petrified him with amazement. For a moment he stood and gaped, unbelievingly, while the owl swooped savagely at his dog. Then, realising that Corrie might be in serious danger, he rushed at the owl with the bushman's saw.

The terrier evaded the Grand Duc's first stroke and jumped up, snarling gamely. The owl, muscle-heavy, had been slow. Corrie rushed after him, leaping and barking; his courage was returning in the face of a recognisable foe. Jock floundered after him, calling him to heel. The Grand Duc turned, ready to swoop again. Jock raised the saw. The owl sheered away, and flapped hovering, as if minded to attack; then discretion tamed his savage heart and he swept back to his roost in the pine tree.

Once the bird had pitched Jock gathered Corrie under an arm and approached the tree, with the bushman's saw held in readiness. For perhaps a minute bird and man stared at each other, the owl looking surprised because owls always look that way, and the man looking amazed because he was. But he had no wish to harm the bird, realising it was just a visitor brought down by the storm, a thing which happened frequently on that wild stretch of moor.

So he left the owl in his tree and ploughed through the snow to the cottage by the loch. Old Tulloch was sceptical about an owl with horns and wings like a goose, and said so.

"Bad whusky can mak a man see auld Nick," he bantered. "It wid be a long-eared owl, Jock, lookin' big in the gloamin'. Or ye've et something!"

"Et be damned!" said Jock. "If it's a long-eared owl somebody must've blawn it up wi' a bicycle pump! I tell ye it went for the dug, man! It's an eagle owl, or the like, blawn in here wi' the storm."

And Jock, as so often happened, was right. Years before he had found a snowy owl in just such weather, and talked about it. The owl now stood on a polished stand, with glass eyes and unruffled feathers, in the doctor's dining-room. Jock had ever afterwards regretted his tactlessness and was determined nobody should learn of this one.

"So," he said to Tulloch, "we'll keep quate, or the artillery'll be oot, an' His Royal Highness'll get his belly stuffed wi' sawdust. We micht never see the like again. Likely he never meant tae come this far. Anyway, he'll gang when the win' chinges, even tho' he biles up hell in the meantime!"

All through the freezing daylight, with its heatless sun-dazzle, the Grand Duc sulked on his perch, morose and famished, opening his flaming eyes from time to time when crow or duck or grouse flew past, and turning his gaze to the sky when a skein of low-flying geese passed over, calling like hounds on a line. Then, in the later afternoon, when the sun was a crimson glare in the misted western sky, he saw a big hare skimming the drifts on snowshoe feet, heading for the Firknowe stack-yard where others of his kind were already nibbling hay.

Boo-hoo!

The hare heard the terrible hoot, sonorous and far-carrying, and full of menace, and knew it came from the throat of no native owl. So he spurned snow, and fled headlong, without waiting to see.

But the Grand Duc was at the peak of his powers again, and

hares were easy game to one who could assault, and slay, the roe deer and giant capercaillies of the northern woods. He swooped after the hare, in wavering flight deceptively swift, and on wings as noiseless as sleep.

Overtaking the fleeing hare the Grand Duc shot up, towering, banked steeply, then swooped with ear tufts flat and talons clutching. The hare, showing teeth, and with ears laid along his back, made one despairing effort to jump away, but suddenly he was enveloped in downy wings and two sets of terrible, knife-edged talons reached for his throat.

The owl's claws cut short the sobbing, child-cries of the hare. The beast scraped snow in the spasms of death while his long cat whiskers gathered rime. Then he was limp and dead, and the alien feasted with the unseemly haste of famine, tearing off great gobs of flesh with his sickle beak and swallowing with much head-shaking and grimacing.

With the life-giving flesh bulging in his craw the Grand Duc returned to his pine roost and dozed till the moon was high and the air had an edge like a knife. He sat for some time afterwards, with eyes closed to slits and breast feathers ruffled over his talons. Then, at the first pinch of hunger, he spread his wings and winnowed away in the direction of his hare.

But the body of the hare was frozen solid, and the Grand Duc was not yet reduced to pecking unrewardingly at frozen flesh. So he leaped into the air and flapped slowly across the moonlit snow to look for other prey.

For an hour he quartered the woods and moor, flying behind and above his own ground shadow, without seeing any sign of life. The grouse were in snug burrows in the snow, and the hares in the stackyards. Then, on the fringe of Glencryan, a sound came to his supersensitive ears that made him check and swerve in flight.

Pat-pat-pat! The sound told of fearless feet padding on the hard snow. The Grand Duc glared down with leopard eyes, and presently made out seven white shapes gliding on the whiter snow. Ermines! These he knew—miniature martens, stoats in winter garb, a pack united by the famine conditions of a white Christmas.

The Grand Duc flapped lower and heard the war-cry of the

questing pack. *Chip-chip-chip*. It was the sound of chipped pebbles. The chipping became angrier as the Grand Duc came down; they had seen him and were threatening. Seven pairs of eyes looked up, and seven pairs of lips were drawn back from needle teeth in snarls of hate. The pack kept moving the while, nose to tail, rippling like caterpillars, fearless and without haste.

Then a cloud fell on them, and a stoat died as the pack scattered and the taint of musk rose heavy on the air. The big owl struck with the speed of a falcon, and was in the air with a stoat clutched in a foot before the pack could rally and leap upon him. But he had no use for ermine. The corded muscles and tainted flesh were repugnant to him—to be eaten only under stress of famine, and he was not famished yet. So he dropped his kill and hovered above the pack, with his round orange eyes staring unwinkingly.

He had a mind to swoop again. But now the stoats were in tight formation, leaping and dancing and tissing, and he knew they would be over him in a body, mauling him, if he made the slightest mistake. Lightning assault, and withdrawal, were now out of the question, so he sheered off and flapped away, remembering again his frozen hare.

He flew in at tree height, and was banking for the drop, when he saw them—two foxes, bellies to snow, side by side, gorging on his hare, while a third padded on a wide circle hoping for leavings. A great anger was born in the Grand Duc's heart. Clicking his sickle beak he made two flapping circuits before swooping to the assault.

The foxes, a mated pair, looked up and leered when they saw the big owl circling above them. With bellies only half full they were not likely to be frightened away by any owl, however huge. Yet they stopped eating, and looked twice, wondering.

Kveck-kveck!

The Grand Duc sounded his battle cry and came in low—bluffing. The foxes rose, with lips curled, flashing ivory, and faced him. But they were bluffing, too, for they realised suddenly that this was no ordinary owl, and were wondering more than ever.

The Grand Duc wheeled, tilted, and came in again—this

time at speed and with both feet forward. The foxes drew back, with teeth bared, convinced now that he was dangerous but confident that they could handle him together. As it happened, they were over-confident. They expected the owl to turn away at the last moment; instead he came right in and struck at the vixen's face. Luckily for her, she turned away instinctively at the moment of contact, and the razor-edged claws raked her neck instead of destroying her eyes.

The dog fox leaped to the attack as the vixen yelped, and spat out two feathers when the Grand Duc bounced upwards, screaming in anger. When the owl swooped again the foxes were no longer there; they were behind him, collecting more of his feathers, and the big owl suddenly realised he was no match for two of them. So he lifted away and flapped round them at tree height, marking time while he weighed chances.

When the two foxes were joined by the third he gave up all idea of assault; the odds were now too great. The foxes had reached a similar conclusion, which is why they allowed the third beast to join them. Even when the owl had disappeared they did not return to the hare to eat; they returned for a moment to mark it with the age-old sign of their contempt. Then they padded away, in case the outlandish bird should return.

Towards daylight the Grand Duc flew down to the hare. The remains were as hard as a board. That alone would not have stopped him now, for he was wild with real hunger; he left it because the foxes, fox-like, had defiled what was left to make sure he wouldn't eat it.

Later, when the sun was high and he was roosting in a warm larch in Glencryan, with half a rabbit in his craw and the other half under his feet, he saw Jock Simpson and Corrie crossing the moor. He didn't know it, but they were following tracks, and reading the stories printed in the snow in the night.

And, while he slept, Jock was telling Tulloch: "Pickle stoat-wheesels on the mair, man! An' wan kilt, likely by His Royal Highness. These feathers'll be his," he went on, showing Tulloch his finds, "an' he's nae moultin'. I got them beside a deid hare where the foxes were stuffin', an' I'm thinkin' there

was some argument. There was a pickle bluid on the snaw, an'
I'm wonderin' whase it is. . . ."

In the snell dawn twilight the Grand Duc was wakened by
the flicking of wings against the larch twigs. He swivelled his
big head round and up, and found himself staring into the
bright eyes of Smokey Joe, the old hoodie, who had pitched
to look at him.

The crow said *Ah-hah!* and chuckled deep in his throat. The
fire kindled in the Grand Duc's eyes, and the fixity of their
stare daunted the usually dauntless crow. He knew this was no
ordinary owl, so he hopped higher up the larch to consider
from a safe distance. Then, as though remembering urgent
business elsewhere, he flew *harking* away. The Grand Duc
threw up a huge pellet, lidded his eyes, and went to sleep with
his beak pressed into his breast and one foot upheld among
ruffled feathers.

But he had not seen the last of Smokey Joe for, soon after
sunrise, he came flapping back, with one hoodie and six
carrion crows at his tail. Only a very bold man would say he
had brought them on a predetermined mission. But any man
who was there would have seen seven yarring crows harrying
and abusing the crouching eagle owl, who could do nothing
more than glare and stare and hope for the best.

They drove him from his roost and chivvied him to the
ground. There he found refuge under a peat overhang, and
there he huddled, beak-clicking and fuming, till the crows tired
and went away. He remained for some time on the ground
before flying back to his larch roost to doze till the sun went
down in a vermilion and apple-green sky.

He flew out at darkening, and when the high-sailing moon
was silvering he circled the loch cottage while his shadow
circled the garden. On a barrow in a junk shed two white hens
were roosting, easy prey for the first caller. The Grand Duc
screighed and flashed into the open shed, and stilled the silly
cackles of both hens before Tulloch ran from the house.
Tulloch, seeing the great bird rising into the air with a big hen
in his feet, swore profanely and gave chase through the garden.
And, suddenly, the hen fell at his feet, for the Grand Duc was

forced to release it before the weight of it pulled him down to the ground.

With nothing more than blood on his tongue, and wisps of feathers sticking to his beak, he flapped into one of the lochside pines to fret and regain his composure.

Tulloch hung the hens up by the feet behind the kitchen door and stood watching the dark bulk of the owl in the tree. The killing of his hens caused him no concern; they were due to be killed for Christmas anyway. But he was curious to know what the big owl would do next.

"Awa an' speir at Simpson's place," he shouted. "He's the man that bids ye welcome!"

The Grand Duc clicked his beak, called *Kveck-kveck*, and fled across the moor towards Firknowe, winnowing low behind his dancing moon shadow.

At intervals through the night he quartered the moor and skirled his war-whoop in the moonlit gloom of Firknowe and Glencryan, without sighting a single quarry. An hour before daybreak he was wild with hunger and in reckless mood. Then he all unwittingly took Tulloch's advice.

He came down near the lighted window of Jock Simpson's cottage when he heard the low talking of hens in the outhouses. Perched on the ridge of a henhouse, with his great horned head limned clear by the back lighting of the moon, he hearkened to the chuckling of the hens and the scurrying of mice feet on the rafters. For a little while he sat motionless on the ridge, staring at the lighted window; then, arching his great wings, he flew to the nearest henhouse.

He circled it twice, soundless as a drifting shadow; but there was no way in. Voiceless, he drifted to the second, and the third; they were sealed against him. The doors of all three were closed, and the open windows covered with protective, fine-mesh wire netting. No bird ever born could have forced an entry. Suddenly, the Grand Duc flew at the nearest window and crashed feet first against the netting. Grappling for a foothold, he anchored himself by the claws and pounded the wire savagely with his wings. He was trying to beat the birds from their cover.

The dread shape at the window—the scratching of claws—

the wild buffering of wings—set the hens cackling and flapping. They long-necked in query; they fought on their perches; they pushed and jostled and crowded into corners. Some fell to the floor, and some took wing, hitting walls and roof. The hen-house became a turmoil of wings and a bedlam of cackling.

The Grand Duc lifted back and up, banked, and crash-flew at the next window, and again he tried to anchor himself by the feet. But this time he got his legs and one wing entangled in a ragged double layer of netting, and before he knew what was happening he was hanging upside down as helplessly as Tulloch's slaughtered hens. That was how Jock Simpson found him a few minutes later when he ran from the house to discover the meaning of the tushkarue.

When he saw the trapped owl Jock whooped in amazement, and called to his wife:

"Come oot! Come oot! We've got Royalty, staunin' on 'is heid. But bring an overcoat."

Jock wrapped the coat round the Grand Duc's head, and carefully extricated his armed feet. He carried the trussed captive to an empty shed, rolled him unceremoniously out on to the floor, and slammed the door. There the big owl knocked himself about for an hour, till all his dignity was gone and only hate and fear remained. When Jock came back later to throw a skinned rabbit into him, he hopped into a corner and glared at it morosely. He did not touch it.

All day he sat in his corner, moping with slitted eyes. With the coming of dusk he flapped and leaped about his prison in a frenzy, battering himself till he was panting and dishevelled. The beating of his wings against door and window kept the hens awake all night, chuckling in query. At seven o'clock in the morning Jock came with a lantern and looked in the window to see the rabbit still untouched and the Grand Duc moping in his corner. He scratched his head in wonder and threw the door wide open.

"Better sterve huntin' for yoursel'," he said, "than dee there wi' grub in front o' your nose. But dinna go back gubblin' like a bubbley-jock at Tulloch's, for ye'll no' be welcome a second time!"

"Whit a burd!" he exclaimed to his wife as the Grand Duc

B

flashed out of the henhouse, lifted over the roof, and flapped away to the pine strip by the loch. "A weel, the wather's on the chinge, so he should get hame directly, afore he fins the smell o' gun poother!"

The Grand Duc pitched in the pine tree where he had made his first landfall, and preened his raggled feathers while Jock Simpson prepared the hens' food in the kitchen.

At daylight, while the owl dozed on his perch, Jock came out to feed his flock in the yard, which he had cleared of snow. They came running to him from all directions—hens, ducks, Chinese geese, and a cocky bantam cockerel the colour of port wine which fed from his hand and spurred the legs of his trousers. The bantam was haughty and fearless. He had ruled the Simpson roost for nearly two years, and Jock was absurdly fond of him because he screeched when foxes made moonlight calls and had once driven a stoat into a hole. No money could have persuaded the fencer to sell his bonny fechter.

The birds scattered after feeding, but only the Chinese geese wandered far; the hens did not like the snow. From his perch, the Grand Duc watched them with brilliant orange eyes, while the wind veered to the south-west and a soft, moist mist cloyed his feathers. The big bird was restless, constantly changing feet, swivelling his head, and blinking his eyes, as if impatient for the coming of dusk.

In the late afternoon, when the light was fading fast, he saw Jock Simpson's Chinese geese stepping in single file towards home. Over the last hundred yards they wasted time dibbling in the snow, and it was just on the edge of dusk when they reached the field behind the cottage. As they started to file through the hedge the Grand Duc left his perch and flew, swift and straight, towards them.

When they saw the dark shape of doom, they hissed and honked and beat their wings in terror. Two ran with spread wings, with webbed feet pattering on the snow, and swished into the air. The Gand Duc clutched at a slim goose, and was ripping her throat when the big gander rushed at him open-beaked, hissing like escaping steam. He turned on the gander, and the bird backed away honking in anger. The clangour of goose voices roused the house, but before Jock was out of the door the Grand Duc, still clutching his goose, had to turn and face a screeching bantam with wings trailing and hackles raised like an umbrella.

Jock saw the bantam jump at the owl with superb courage. He saw it received in a great, clawed foot and crushed to death without a fight. Then the Grand Duc lifted lightly into the air with his prey, glad to leave the heavy body of the goose which he could not have carried away in a week of trying. Jock, ignoring the dead goose, watched him fly out of sight in the gloaming, with the bantam hanging limp from his claws. At that moment there was a great anger in the man.

Afterwards, when he was sitting on the chopping block plucking the goose with practised fingers, his wife came out to him. She did not speak of the bantam. Instead she said:

"Well?"

"He'd best be awa hame," he said, without looking up. "A widna want tae herm him, but . . . he'd best keep trevlin' north afore A blaw his Royal brains oot."

The Grand Duc had really hit Jock Simpson where it hurt.

The Red Stranger

IT was cubbing time in the big badger cairn on the Ben of Mists, though the snow still lay deep in the high corries and swept in clouds of white powder before the savage, scourging winds on the tops. Up there, among the rocks, the naked aspen roots were still clawed with icicles, and every mountain cascade was silent, the falling waters turned to columns and pillars of ice that glowed with rainbow fire in the sun.

Countless generations of badger cubs had been born in the wild, rocky cairn, the age or depth of which no man knew—for a badger sett can be old as a town is old, and as steeped in history.

The den on the Ben of Mists knew the *broc* when the Great Marquis swept down the Garry to Athole. Dundee had rested where the badgers foraged before his falcon swoop to victory and death at Killiecrankie. And, later still, but still two centuries ago, the sunning brocks had hearkened to the faint, far skirl of the Highland War Pipes when the clansmen marched to death and exile under the banner of Royal Tearlach.

That morning the sun was bright in a sky of vitreous blue and Bodach, the old boar badger, king of the cairn, was lying in a grassy hollow, sucking a forepaw, sunning himself out of the wind. Night hunter though he was, and born of a line that had prowled by night for a thousand years, he still liked the feel of the sun, and in that quiet stronghold on the Ben of Mists he could afford the risk of such a luxury.

The cairn was in an oakwood, on a great knuckle of ground rising steeply from the glen. There the wind was always slight, and the sun's rays warm. The crowded oaks—dark, damp, mossgrown, lichened and arthritic—baffled the fury of the wildest winter gales, and their harvest of acorns was devoured each year by the badgers. Deer sheltered in the wood when the wind raked the tops with its icy talons, and the snow was churned by their hooves, stained with their droppings, and scraped where they had rested or fed.

Bodach removed his forepaw from his mouth, rolled on to a hip, and licked under his armpit. The skin was scuffed there, by a slip on a rock in the night, and the frost was pricking. The licking was soothing and Bodach closed his eyes. But not his ears; or his nose. And, suddenly, his striped head was up, high, darting from side to side like a snake's. Deer were running in the wood.

They came on through the trees in a rush, with thud and swish of hooves—knobbers, brockets, and proud high-antlered harts—with nostrils flared and flanks heaving in growing panic. They surged up to the first rocks of the cairn. They turned broadside, and halted. In one movement they swung their heads, and froze, to face downhill, breathing vapour. Ten paces to the front, facing square to his own trail, stood a little knobber, with ears forward, scouting for the herd. Bodach blinked, and sat on his scut. Twenty-seven deer and one badger waited, motionless, for the space of ten heart-beats—the deer alarmed and uneasy, the badger alerted but un-afraid. And there was a mighty rush of wings above the cairn.

Bodach crouched. The deer crashed away. An immense shadow flashed across the discoloured snow, and the eagle was down—*swoosh!* And up—*swoosh!* At tree height he heeled over and came down again, and the deer broke in wild stampede from the wood. But the eagle was not swooping to the assault; he was pitching to roost, and rest. As the deer bounded away through the trees in clouds of misted breath, he swung up to the top of the cairn, to a great leaning rock as big as a sheiling, and reached for it with feet like grappling irons. When his yellow, black-clawed talons secured their grip he folded his vast wings, and blinked. On the rock were one of his pellets and three of his breast feathers to betray it as a roosting place.

The eagle closed his eyes, and lifted one set of talons into the feathers of his belly. Bodach crouched, muzzle on forepaws, motionless, alert, still suspicious. He knew the eagle. He had seen the bird take wing from the rock in the chill of many dawns. He was not afraid of him. But he could not be sure that it was the eagle who had alarmed the deer. So he sat on— listening, smelling, looking. There was no movement on the churned and slotted snow. Then a grey crow flapped down, and swaggered about the scrapes, and pecked at dark, shiny deer droppings, and Bodach knew there was no kind of peril close at hand.

Relaxing, Bodach turned on his seat, then shambled up through the boulders, by well-worn tracks, to one of the entrance holes to the sett. It was under a high, leaning rock, screened by down-spreading aspens rooted in a dark, vertical cleft. Icicles thick as the talons of the eagle reached down over the entrance, long as otter tails and tipped like the horns of a roe. Bodach thrust in under the icicles, and turned about, breaking them off like dry twigs. He scooped them away with a paw and squatted at the mouth of the sett, with his rump inside and his face out in the sun. The mewing of a buzzard, the *prukking* of ravens, the harsh yarring of crows, were familiar sounds. He sucked a paw, and drowsed.

Below him, far inside the cairn, his mate lay curled with her three small helpless cubs, on a fresh, sweet bed of withered bracken and young grass which she had laboriously carried into the den. The galleries of the den were long and tortuous, and in their dark shelter lay two other female badgers nursing cubs. In all, the sett held three nursing sows; three boars which were their mates; and two young males of the previous year. And Bodach was the chief by virtue of age and prowess.

The wind eddied into Bodach's hollow in spent breaths, ruffling the grey hair of his back and bringing messages to his wet nose. And, quite suddenly, he awoke with a start, grunting and releasing his paw, for his nose had just owned a scent that he didn't like—a scent that spelt trouble.

Over the ice-feathered rocks of the cairn came a big hill vixen, red of leg and long of jaw, with her tongue out and her brush down, hirpling along on three legs. Bodach smelt her strong musky odour; he could also smell her blood. But it is doubtful if he realised that her left forepaw was a bloody stump which throbbed more agonisingly than an aching tooth. The big vixen had just chewed herself from a gin set by the keeper, and had left three toes and four nails behind.

And now she was seeking refuge in the cairn of the badgers!

Bodach didn't like her. And he didn't want her. But when she crawled into the hole above him, leaving blood spots on the snow, he made no move to stop her.

Perhaps he realised she was wounded; he may even have realised that she would be sought after by the man who had set the gin. He had had foxes in the sett before, and didn't like their dirty habits, their way of cluttering up the pipes with bits and pieces of prey. In the past, he had tolerated such lodgers for a time, then driven them out with threatening jaws. Yet, on this occasion, he appeared to be quite indifferent to the presence of a wounded fox who was wanted by Man!

The old badger sat for some minutes after the vixen disappeared, swaying from side to side like a bear; then he slouched underground to join his mate, who had already got news of the vixen with her nose and knew a fox was in the cairn.

The red stranger crawled slowly down a side tunnel, one which was not being used by the badgers, but which was really a graveyard for the clan; for many dead badgers were walled up in the tunnel, carefully buried from sight in side pockets dug by the feet of Bodach and his ancestors. The vixen found an unlined hollow beneath an outcrop of rock and lay down to lick her stouning foot.

No badger came to her during all that day, but she heard the clan leaving after dusk on their hunting trips. Throughout the night she did not stir from the cairn, being too preoccupied with her aching foot. At first light she heard water running in a quick thaw and went out to lap. Her paw was swollen and throbbing and would not be soothed by her tongue. When dusk came she was still lying nose to flank, with the injured paw laid carefully on her muzzle and pain shooting up her leg like a current. She spent the second night lying up, with neither food nor water. By midday the pain in her foot lessened, and she was racked by the pain of hunger. Her flanks dimpled and flickered; she, too, was about to become a mother. But how could she hope to hunt in her condition?

Such thoughts may not have occurred to her, but she certainly made no effort to strike out on her own when she at last left the cairn. Instead, she took up the trail of Bodach, and followed it. She was going to play jackal to the badger. . . .

That night Bodach went right down into the glen, where the red deer were scraping through to grass along the river. He knew it was useless hunting upwards, for wind and snow had driven everything down except the ptarmigan. The badger followed the rutted lane ploughed by the deer in the snow. And the vixen, limping on three legs, followed the badger, keeping in touch with her nose.

The lower slopes were cleared forest, and big herds of deer were feeding among millions of tree stumps and along avenues of layered, weathered branches. Mountain hares were feeding there; but they were too fleet for Bodach and he ignored them. The vixen's jaws dripped water but she knew she had no hope of hunting hares for many nights to come.

Bodach gobbled beetles which he found by ripping into the matted layers of branches with his claws. Then he found the remains of a grouse that had been killed by a falcon, and squatted down to eat it, warning off the vixen with grunts and a clicking display of teeth. She made no move to interfere. She was content to wait.

And, in due course, her patience was rewarded. Bodach found the entrance to a rabbit's nest, or stop, under a clutter of old branches. He sniffed at the sealed entrance, scraped away a little of the peaty soil, and satisfied himself there were rabbits inside. But he didn't start to dig at the mouth of the burrow.

Instead, he crashed into the foiling branches and started to heave them aside with his powerful forepaws. When he had cleared a space in which he could manœuvre, he started to dig straight down. The now thin frost-crust delayed his tearing claws for only a moment, and soon the sand and pebbles and roots were flying past his flank. He was digging a shaft right down on to the rabbit's nest.

In a few minutes he had the nest uncovered. A few seconds more, and he was clawing the young rabbits, blind and naked, from their bed of grass and wool. The vixen sat impassively while he was digging; but when he had scattered five young rabbits on the branches she moved in to mooch.

At first, Bodach grunted at her, like a rooting hog. But once he was settled, chewing on one rabbit while holding down two others with his claws, he let her sneak in to filch the remaining pair. Snarling, she drew back; and she had bolted both rabbits before Bodach started on his second. The food was a godsend to her, for she could not have dug out the rabbits herself; but, instead of appreciating the badger's generosity, she tried to snatch a third rabbit from under his jaws.

Bodach, however, had had enough of her, and when he rose, showing his teeth, she knew she had gone as far as she dared. With a parting snarl at her benefactor she turned away and limped slowly back to the cairn, leaving Bodach on his own for the rest of the night.

And so it was, night after night, for the next week: the vixen was Bodach's shadow. Not once did she follow the other boar badgers, or the nursing sows. It was always Bodach; and the old badger never tried to drive her away.

Of course, when he found food, he always warned her off; and if there was not enough for two she had to go without. In this way she eked out a living, but it didn't make her fat, for Bodach spent as much time in the low woods digging for blue-bell bulbs as he did ranging the glen for rabbit nests or carrion. And when he was on vegetable food like that, as he often was, the vixen had to go to bed with an empty belly.

One night, when Bodach went foraging uphill, he found the remains of a red deer hind, on which the ravens and crows had been feasting for days. Fox and badger ate their fill of old venison that night and afterwards the vixen drank greedily. It was the stoutest meal she had eaten for more than a week. But when she went back the following night, without the badger, she found that the last remains had been eaten by the carrion birds during the day.

Disgruntled, her thoughts turned at once to Bodach, so she limped away to seek him in the glen. It was close on daybreak before she found him, carrying in his jaws the fore-end of a mountain hare—the remains, or rather the unwanted half, of an eagle's prey. The bird was perched on the big rock above the badger sett with the haunches under his feet.

Bodach knew the daylight was not far off, so he was carrying his prey to a spot nearer home where he could devour it without worrying about the time. He had a strong objection to being caught far from home in daylight. The vixen could not get near him on the way home. Time after time he stopped to grunt at her and she was too wise to force her attentions on him. In a hollow about a hundred yards from the cairn, Bodach finally stopped and lay down to eat his meal, for it was against all his cleanly principles to take food right into the den.

When he had eaten all he could hold, he left the remains of his prey and hurried home as fast as his short legs could take him. The vixen at once snatched up the leavings, girning slit-eyed as she did so. And, being a fox, she had none of the badger's scruples, so she carried the prey to the cairn and vanished inside with it in her jaws.

Now, if she had been well enough to keep bringing prey home like that, it is probable that Bodach would have thrown her out for her dirty housekeeping. However, before she could commit a second offence, badgers and fox had other things to worry about.

One morning the dwellers in the cairn heard the ominous tread of nailed boots on the rocks above, then the voices of men, followed by the sharp yelping of terriers. The sow badgers cuddled closer to their cubs; four boars crouched wondering; the vixen drew back into the narrowest neck of the tunnel.

Bodach mounted guard at the main entrance to the nurseries. Bodach was old. He knew what was coming. And he knew how to deal with it.

Above ground were two keepers, the shepherd, and two varminty terriers. The keepers had no quarrel with the badgers, and were doubtful about letting the dogs into the sett to try to bolt the fox. They knew what a baited badger could do to a terrier.

"She had to pick the badger sett, of course!" grumbled MacDonald, the head keeper, rubbing his chin reflectively.

"Weel, there it is," commented the shepherd. "It was pure chance I was spying down this way, and there she was on the rocks, sore foot and all. What d'you think, Mac?"

"She'll no' trap, that's certain!" interjected Fraser, the under-keeper. "That foot's a' the lesson she needs tae mak her leery o' them."

MacDonald was perturbed. He was ruthless with foxes, but hated all unnecessary killing. He liked badgers. But he also liked his terriers.

"If the brocks stay clear the dogs micht bolt her," he said. "But they'll ha'e cubs, and I canna see them standing by idle if the dogs take the wrong road. God knows how many holes and corners are doon there. Still, I suppose we'll have tae try."

The first dog was slipped—a small, lean Border terrier with a much-scarred mask. Her name was Tarf. Fearlessly, she darted into the den, and the men posted themselves on the rocks, with shotguns at the ready.

Down below, there was fear among the badgers; but no panic. The sows started digging frantically, to put earth and distance behind them; the boars dug—all except Bodach, who stood four-square on the threshold of the nurseries; the red vixen waited, hoping. . . .

But the vixen was unlucky. The terrier, knowing her business, found the tunnel leading to the fox, and by-passed the waiting badger. She went warily, till the funk reek of fox was strong in her nostrils. And, presently, her frenzied barking came faint and muffled to the men, telling them she had found her fox.

The big vixen drew back hard against the wall of the tunnel, and presented her sharp muzzle to the foe. Her lips were lifted, showing her long, sharp tusks. Tarf rushed in, chopping and girning, but the vixen met her teeth to teeth and cut her slash for slash. Blood appeared on the fox's mask, but not all of it was her own. Realising she couldn't get behind the fox, Tarf crouched down, yapping harshly, trying to stampede her opponent into some kind of forward move. But the vixen was cunning; she had been baited before. She was content to leave the offensive to the dog.

The terrier's frenzied yapping, faint though it was, told the men much. They knew the vixen was cornered, but refusing to bolt.

"We'll leave her a wee," said MacDonald, who realised the dog had only the fox to deal with.

For several minutes dog and fox faced each other—the little bitch barking, the vixen mute. Then Tarf, always volatile and fiery, worked herself into such a pitch of rage that she darted to the clinch. The fox's teeth opened the skin above her eye; they cut her ear; they clashed against her tusks. But, blind to the bites, and roused to a fury of suicidal recklessness, Tarf was in and under, gurrying through the vixen's ruff for her throat.

Her teeth found skin, and gripped, and closed. The vixen chop-chopped at her attacker's flank, scoring it with her tusks; but she could not reach round far enough for a wounding bite. She knew the dog's grip was fatal if she could not shake it off. And she could not retreat. So she moved forward, taking the terrier with her. They fought along the tunnel, a locked, squirming mass of fur, with Tarf hanging on grimly, growling through locked teeth as she worried. Presently, they were in a wider part of the tunnel, where the vixen could move faster. In her blind rush for the open, she rubbed against a projecting rock. The rock stabbed Tarf in the ribs, and she was scraped from her hold. And the vixen was free.

But . . .

What was this blocking the way out? A badger! It was Bodach himself, filling the tunnel with his bulk, standing there with head lowered, waiting. . . .

For what? For the fox? No, not for the fox, for he let the vixen squeeze past him without demur. In fact, he drew in against the wall to let her through. He was waiting for the dog!

Game though she was, Tarf was no match for the big boar badger of the Ben of Mists, especially in her weakened state. And she knew it. But the knowledge did not deter her, and she shaped up to Bodach, bristling, with teeth bared to the gums —a brave fighter meeting another brave fighter with all the advantages of size and ground on the badger's side.

At the first clash, Tarf's jaws gathered nothing but grey hair from the badger's shoulder. But Bodach's jaws tore skin and flesh from her face, and her howling was heard by the men at the den mouth above. For a moment they could not understand what was happening; then they saw the vixen near the mouth of the den before she turned into another tunnel. And they knew Tarf was face to face with a badger.

"She's on to a brock!" said MacDonald. "And maybe behind him, whatever. Send in Sheila, quick!"

Sheila knew what was expected of her, and needed no encouragement. She was in like a flash, and down, hurrying to the help of the kennel mate who was her mother. And, in a few seconds, she was behind the badger.

Now, a badger's hide is thick and tough, and the teeth of a terrier do not make much impression on it. But a badger has also one weak spot; a spot he doesn't like touched at all—his scut. He is sensitive about his little tag of a tail. Bodach was no exception. When he felt Sheila's teeth at his tail he swung round to face her.

She backed away, of course, and he charged at her, chopping with his terrible teeth. But he now had two terriers to deal with, and no sooner was he engaged with Sheila than he felt other teeth at his scut. So he had to keep thrusting forward, to find a place where he could get them both in front of him.

Bodach didn't panic. It was not his nature. He was a stoic, a gentleman, and brave as they come. But this tail was worrying him. He had to get it out of reach of the dogs. The terriers, on the other hand, knew they had him at a disadvantage, and meant to keep him there. So, while the bitch at the rear, the gallant little Tarf, kept worrying at Bodach's scut, Sheila kept biting, and getting bitten, at his front.

But it could not last. Bodach turned suddenly, realising he

could rush Tarf to the blind end of the tunnel and worry her there. He swept her before him, irresistibly. It seemed she must at last die down there, below the wild rocks of the cairn, with no one to come to her aid. But there was still Sheila!

As if realising the badger's intention, she leaped at his rump, and worried and bit till she really stung him to anger. For the first time in his life Bodach was being worsted. So he turned yet again to deal with the attacker at his back. In that instant Tarf rushed at him again and, whether by accident or intention, squeezed past him to join Sheila at the front.

The dogs were now assured of a line of retreat; the exit was at their back. It was as well for them that this was so, for Bodach now had them where he wanted them—in front of him. With his rear secure, he kept inching towards them, with his sharp face well down, striking to right and left with the speed of a viper, forcing them to yield ground or run the risk of a broken jaw. The terriers yapped, and snarled, but kept edging slowly backwards, for they had no way of getting round Bodach's guard, and they knew the terrible punishing power of his teeth.

As they neared the mouth of the set, Bodach speeded up his attack, carrying the fight right to the dogs. The first inkling the waiting men had of the truth was when the terriers came hurrying out backwards, closely followed by a big badger reaching for their throats.

MacDonald instantly called off the dogs. They came bellying up to him reluctantly, with teeth bared and hackles up. The keeper swore when he saw how they were cut up, then turned to where Bodach crouched, watching, with chin up and the light of battle in his small, bright eyes.

"Don't shoot him!" MacDonald shouted to Fraser, who had raised his gun. Then he turned to the crouching badger. "Take that, you auld scunner, you!" he said, and he set Bodach in motion with a well-placed toe on his seat. "Now, get the hell out of it!"

Bodach blinked, and kept moving. He shambled into the sett, affronted at the indignity, but suddenly aware of the perilous proximity of men. Their presence terrified him as no number of dogs could ever do.

"What now?" asked Fraser, the under-keeper. "Traps?"

"Not here," MacDonald said. "We'd only take the brocks. The fox would push them out first. You'll have to try baited traps in the peat hags. That bitch'll be looking for easy meat for a whiley yet."

Bodach heard the men and dogs depart, but did not come out to watch them go.

Three traps, baited with grouse, were set during the afternoon, on built-up hummocks in peat hags, on to which a fox would have to jump to reach the prize. And no fox could touch them without having a foot gripped by teeth of steel. But, as it happened, the jaws of the traps waited in vain for the vixen's feet.

That night a blizzard raged out of the north, turning the tops to a swirling white chaos and muffling the glens under a thick mantle of new snow. It blew itself out on the afternoon of the second day, and only then did fox and badgers emerge to view the world. The tops were white, the cold intense, and the moon rising clear in a starry sky as dark as a raven's wing.

Bodach mooched about the cairn, sinking belly deep in the dry, powdery snow. He clawed and heaved his way up to the eagle's rock, and below it found part of a hare, which he proceeded to eat. He was joined after a little while by his mate, who ate with him, then by the big vixen, at whom they grunted in warning. She did not force the issue, though she was wild with hunger. She played the waiting game, hoping for leavings. But when Bodach and his mate slid back down over the rocks there was nothing left for her, and all she could do was drool and fume in anger.

About midnight, the frost put a hard crust on the snow and Bodach shambled off along the mountainside, with only a vague idea of where he was going. At worst he would scrape through the snow for grass and blaeberries in the glen. He was followed by his own distorted shadow. And, on the heels of his shadow, printing her own neat foot-sign alongside the badger's bear-like presses, limped the big red vixen.

Right into trouble. . . .

They were on the lip of a small corrie, following a deer path already slotted by hooves since the snowfall, when the pack-cry reached their ears. It came faintly at first, like the chipping of flints, strangely but unmistakably menacing.

Bodach stopped, arcing his snout like a bear. The vixen halted, rigid, with ears up and nose questing. Soon the cry became louder, clearer, followed by musk smell, crimson dots of eyes flickering in the moonshine, then the rippling movements of stoats gliding over the snow: sixteen of them—some still white, some on the change to russet, but all wild with famine, all dangerous, a family united by hunger.

They met Bodach first, because Bodach was in front. They swarmed round him, and over him, hissing, spitting, chattering, with needle teeth bared and black-tipped tails rigid. Bodach crouched, with hind feet drawn well in and head down, waiting. The big dog stoat who was the leader of the pack chattered loudly, and they broke over Bodach in a wave.

The badger moved only his black-striped head—and his jaws. He kept his hindlegs in because he had no wish to be hamstrung. Stoats bit at his back, his head, his rump; but his hide was impervious to their teeth. They hissed in his ears. Their musk scent nauseated him. But while they fumed he was chopping. He broke the backs of three stoats in thirty seconds, while the remainder were gathering mouthfuls of grey, bristly hair.

With three stoats kicking and doing a death dance in the snow, Bodach was prepared to sit till those on his back came within reach of his jaws. He knew he could not carry the fight to such will-o'-the-wisps. But, presently, they became more selective in their attacks. They found his ears—and his scut. They bit both. They stung him to white-hot fury. He rose to fight. And, instantly, they were round his legs, under his guard, under his scut.

He killed two more, and bit snow to get the horrible taste from his mouth. Then he started to spin round, reaching for the others with his jaws.

At that moment, the red vixen intervened. She had been sitting on her tail twenty paces away, sizing up the situation. She could have retreated. She had time. But she didn't. Inexplicably, she went voluntarily into the fight.

Her long jaws were lightning swift. She was agile, despite

her crippled foot. No slow-moving, stoical badger this! She chopped two more stoats and in so doing diverted the attack to herself. As the rest leaped at her she drew back to keep them at her front, and waited for them with tusks bared and amber eyes closed to slits.

She was on the brink of the corrie when they struck her, where the snow was sculpted into eaves by the wind. She met them with snapping jaws, with wounded forepaw raised as a guard. As she snatched one in her jaws, three flashed in and had her by jowl and ruff. Then the snow-eaves gave way. . . .

For a moment the mass of snow seemed to hang in the air above the corrie; then it fell clear, and down, and the vixen, with three stoats at her neck and one falling from her jaws, went with it, spinning and kicking with brush flying. Bodach crouched in the blood-stained snow, looking, listening, wondering—long after he heard the muffled thud on the rocks sixty feet below.

The red stranger had paid her debt in full.

c

The Ben Dearg Royal

Tri aois coin, aois eich
Tri aois eich aois duine
Tri aois duine aois feidh
Tri aois feidh aois fir-eoin
Tri aois fir-eoin aois craoibhe-dharaich.

THRICE the age of a dog, the age of a horse; thrice the age of a horse, the age of a man; thrice the age of a man, the age of a stag; thrice the age of a stag, the age of an eagle; thrice the age of an eagle, the age of an oak-tree. Thus the old rhyme of the Gael. And in the Highlands today the ear can still listen to rhyme, ignoring research, and hear the great tales of olden times: when the proud, high-antlered harts were the quarry of kings; when King James V, with twelve thousand men, killed eighteen score harts in Teviotdale and thirty score in Athole, along with roe and roebuck, wolf and fox and wildcat; when two thousand Athole men, gathering the deer in Mar and Badenoch, Athole and Murray, could drive a herd, numbering a beast for every man of them, to delight the eye of that Mary of Scots who died at the hand of Elizabeth of England.

They tell yet, in the forests, of the milk-white hind of Loch Treig, that MacDonald of Tulloch knew: she who was never fired at and who lived for a hundred and sixty years in the wilds of Lochaber. In Badenoch roamed the Great Stag—the Damh Mor of the legend—who lived for two hundred years. Always there are stories of the great beasts of bygone days: who roamed the ancient forests through many reigns; who outlived the Chief and his sons; who were young when men had grown old. The kings and the chiefs have gone; only the deer remain. And the legends.

But the legends—thrice the age of a horse, the age of a man; thrice the age of a man, the age of a stag—are dying under the remorseless scrutiny of modern research; and the life of a stag can be measured by the rise and decline of his antlers, as a salmon's is measured by the scales, or a tree's by the rings of growth. At twelve, the Highland stag is in his prime—a Royal if ever he is going to be one; thereafter he begins to fail in prowess and antlers, and is old before men have attained to manhood.

In the wild, there is no place for the aged and the ailing. In the days of the great Forest, when Scotland was a kingdom, the wolf harried the deer herds as wolves today harry the caribou of the tundra: keeping them fleet and strong, so that death by time and the misery of age were alike unknown. Today, man kills the deer selectively, for the wolf has gone; the stalker, treading the remote places with glass and rifle, grasses with a bullet the ailing and the old, the barren and the unsightly.

But the red deer has fallen on evil days. Like the great falcons, once the pride of kings, he has been reduced to the status of vermin: without protection or Close Season; butchered by gangsters; execrated by sheep-men; a pawn in the hands of political jugglers; disowned by Governments— honoured only by those who stalk him, and by the few who would still preserve something of our heritage of beauty in the wild places long raped by greed and disfigured by the massive and monstrous surgery of industrialism.

The great Caledonian Forest that the Romans knew has

gone; the deer forests of the twentieth century are treeless barrens, home of mountain fox and marten, wildcat and eagle, into which the new woods of spruce and larch and pine, planted by a new generation of men, creep slowly. The wild glens, the naked slopes and the high ridges are the territory of the red deer; true descendants of the great beasts of the Pleistocene: the largest and noblest land mammals surviving in Britain.

And this is the story of a little stag calf who grew up to be a royal.

Damh Mor—the Royal stag of Ben Dearg—first saw the light in a sheltered, sun-facing hollow below the crag of the eagles. Along the slope were other grassy terraces, gently sloping, where hinds were moving, awaiting the miracle of birth, for this was a calving place as far back as man can remember. Below stretched lonely Glen Eilid—the glen of the hinds—remote, wild, boulder-strewn: treeless as far as eye could see. Blue and blood-red and purple were the mountains in the sun-rise, with light and shadow creeping, and ravens croaking in dark ravines where wild waters rushed.

At birth, the calf was an awkward, sprawling bundle of legs, unable to lift his sleek head, unable to sit up, unable to stand; wet and squirming; snorting and choking with the gleet in his mouth. Until the sun rose clear above the mountains his mother stood over him, *ba-aing* softly and hoarsely in her throat, and licking him without pause. Her warm tongue, gentle, expert and soothing, lick-licked till she had his brown coat waved and dried. Only then did the calf manage to get his long legs under some kind of control, sitting up with them gathered against his flank while he reached up to tongue his mother's face.

But the hind did not linger for his caresses; nor did she give him any mothering after licking him dry. Instead, she pressed him gently but firmly with her muzzle to impress upon him that he must not rise, or struggle, or make any sound while she was gone. Then she left him, trotting out of the hollow at leisurely pace and disappearing over the rise at the top. Out of his sight, but within earshot, she stood with head high and ears erect, seeking signs of danger before she lowered her head to graze.

The calf lay, chin to ground, after she had gone, unmoving except for a tremor over ribs following a deeper breath. Without twitch of ear, he listened; hearing without understanding, the song of a mountain blackbird, the *chakking* of wheatears, the prukking of a raven, and the faint mewing of a buzzard soaring about the peak of Ben Dearg. The sun was on him— the hour-old calf, unsuckled; but the soft eyes glowed without highlight under sweeping lashes.

At ground level, grass and heather tufts hid him, but from above he was conspicuous in his snow-flaked coat. Yet, unmoving, he was visible only to the most selective eyes, like the eyes of man. The eyes of the wild kindred of the hills are not highly selective; they see form mostly in movement or unaccustomed silhouette. So lying still was, for the deer calf, to lie unnoticed, and it was the thing he could do above all others. Without being able to think about it, he knew it was the price of survival.

Six times during the morning an immense shadow wavered along the ground before his eyes: the mighty shadows of eagles flying to and from their eyrie on the Eagle Rock where they had two white, hungry eaglets. The royal birds knew the calf was there somewhere, for they had seen him in the hour of struggling, but they made no move to molest him. They were carrying grouse and mountain hare to their eaglets, mounting buoyantly with the prey in their feet.

Twice during the long afternoon, and again in the hour before sunset, the hind came to him. By then, he was familiar with the eagles, the ravens, and the gentle blue hares hopping about the hollow on snow-shoe feet. Each time he heard the tread of his mother, he shrank visibly; then, recognising her, he gave a feeble bleat, struggled up on to his long rubbery legs, and wobbled towards her to nurse.

In a few days his legs were strong and he capered around his mother for a little while after nursing. On the fourth day of his life he touched noses with another little wobbly calf, also born in the hollow, who was trying out his legs under the watchful eyes of his mother. It was then that Damh Mor, the royal-to-be, noticed yet other calves on the green terraces, all about his own age. There were five within range of his seeing. But no hind yet allowed her calf to run with her. After the brief period of nursing and play, each was muzzled firmly on the rump and made to lie still. Scudding clouds, sunlit, dappled the hills; on the tops the wind was cold. But Damh Mor slept warm in the hollow, which the wind passed over.

Such was the pattern of his early days: long spells on his own, lying muzzle to flank on his couch; short visits from his mother; the close crouch when some new sound or movement was introduced to his life. He was not troubled by loneliness. For the moment, it was his way of life, and he would not have called out for his mother except in extreme emergency. The emergency arose when he was a week old. . . .

A big Highland wildcat—a female giant of frame and terrible of tusks—skulked into the hollow at mid-morning when Ben Dearg was cloud-capped. She came flat-eared and grimacing, long-whiskered and green-eyed, with ringed tail twitching. Far down the glen, in the dead calm of daybreak, she had been roused to flight by three yapping terriers, urged on to bay her by two men in tweeds. The dogs had harassed and hunted her, from cairn to cairn and scree to scree, driving her far out of her way and leaving the men behind. But she had shaken them off at last by a huge leap over a treacherous gorge, and now she was homing late, full of grouse meat and anger, to her kits in a cairn over the shoulder of Ben Dearg.

With the wind at her back, and her moon eyes on Ben Dearg, she was almost on top of the calf before she saw him. She hissed and recoiled, with one forepaw raised and thick tail brushing the heather. The calf shuddered and blinked. Here was visual peril—beside him, aware of him: clawed, tusked and poised to strike. With a wild cry he struggled to his feet. The cat clawed his face with a fore-stroke as he rose, and leaped sideways to clitch on to him as he bolted. Her hind-claws raked his flank, but she could not pull him down; she fell, winded and spitting. And the hind rushed into the hollow.

Fergus Stewart, the stalker, booted and gaitered, in check two-snooter, with glass and rifle slung over his shoulder, topped the knowe above the hollow with three terriers at heel. Behind him walked the under-keeper, a MacRae from Kintail, in leather jacket and peaked cap, with side-pack slung and a ·22 Winchester in the crook of his arm. One dog had a bleeding lip—a claw-stroke from the wildcat—and all three were winded.

Stewart inched his eyes slowly above the rise—the old stalking trick of seeing the ears of deer without being seen; then he heard the terrified crying of a calf, and rushed over the top. What he saw was a calf running in circles, crying in terror, and a hind stamping after a wildcat, dab-dabbing with her hooves. The stalker started to run downhill, unslinging the rifle, and calling to MacRae at his back:

"Come quickly, Donald! It iss the big cat again, with a hind chasing her, whateffer!"

Fifty yards from the hollow Stewart bellied down, with his cheek to the Mannlicher. The hind was driving the cat uphill, striking at her with a foot; but, even in the heat of the chase, she winded the man above her, and stopped short with ears pointing to the sky. The cat weaved on through heather and rocks, up and up, an impossible target. The hind, running to her calf, tried to drive him from the hollow, but he collapsed with all four legs splayed, wailing and exhausted.

Jumping to his feet Stewart waved the dogs out after the wildcat. Then he turned to MacRae:

"Donald," he said; "you go on after the dogs, while I look to see how the calvie is. We don't know but the cat might have hurted him."

The hind bounded left and right across his front as he hurried down, trying to draw him away. Then she barked once and disappeared below the hollow. Laying down the Mannlicher, Stewart knelt beside the panting calf and tucked up the sprawled legs. The little Damh Mor had claw marks dangerously close to an eye, and there was blood on his face. His flanks were slashed, but not irreparably; they would scar. The stalker gouged a handful of wet peat from a sap with his fingers, and applied it thickly to the flank wounds. "That will keep away the flies, maybe," he said. Then, with his gralloching knife, he cut a clean, right-angled piece from the calf's left ear.

Rising, he wiped his peaty and bloodied hands on his thighs, and unslung his glass. High above him, he could make out Donald among the rocks, with the terriers on a higher shelf, marking at a horizontal cleft. Stewart patted the calf, slung his rifle, and started up the ridge. The barking of the terriers came to him: harsh, savage barks that told him the cat was cornered. Waywise, and tireless of stride, he was soon beside Donald among the jumbled rocks.

"They have her under a shelf up there," Donald told him. "But they can't get near her, whatever, for aye the paw comes out to mak' them yelp."

"I lug-marked the calvie," Stewart said. "Now let us see what iss going on here. Tarf! Sionnach! Sandy!" he called off the dogs. "Come here and sit ye doon!"

They came to him, tail-wagging—Tarf the terrible, black and wheaten, three-quarters Border; Sionnach, the varminty pure-bred Border with the otter face; Sandy the shaggy Cairn, who had killed more than fifty fox cubs—and sat at his feet, tongues flacking. All three had blood globules on their masks where the cat's lightning claws had struck.

Stewart knelt beside the cleft in the rock. He pulled a heather tuft from the rock and dragged it along the ground. Immediately an armed forepaw shot out, pat-pat-patting at the bait. Laughing, Stewart rose, and tipped back his check two-snooter.

"Now if we had a bit rope, Donald," he said, "a man might get a hitch on that paw and haf her out. But then if a man had no rope," he went on, "he couldn't. Haf you a rope, Donald?"

"No, Fergus, I haf not; but I haf binder twine, which will be strong enough I'm thinking."

"Och, well then," said Stewart, "maybe we'd better see what we can do, but they're precarious beasts to be handling whateffer."

So they fashioned a running knot, and baited the cat, and after many misses they succeeded in catching her by the paw. She yowled and hissed and spat; she made noises like fire crackling in dry bracken. The terriers, growling, rushed at her and had to be cuffed and booted to their seats. Stewart pulled steadily on the leg, inviting her to hold against him, not wishing

to jerk out a bristling, clawing fiend among his feet. She fought
against him inch by inch, screaming and snarling, but presently
her head was drawn clear of the cleft. She faced them with ears
flat and teeth bared, hissing explosively—unblinking, un-
tameable, magnificent in her fury. Stewart eased the pull on
the string, allowing her to recoil a little, with her head against
the rock.

"Now!" he said.

Donald, kneeling, shot her with the ·22. The bullet cut short
her screeching. She leaped into the air, fell, somersaulted, and
lay kicking in the heather. Blood oozed from between her
flaming eyes. She quivered, and was still. Her mask was terrible
in death. Once more the stalker had to cuff off the dogs, who
were eager to worry her.

"She is being sooked, Donald," he said. There was regret in
his voice. He tailed the cat with his knife.

"Yes," said Donald. "That will be a litter less for sure.
There iss no wild tom cares a damn for his kits."

With the cat's tail in Donald's side-pack, they left with the
dogs to check the fox dens on Ben Dearg; the body they threw
among the rocks. In the heat of the day the flies found the
carcase, and soon they were crowding on the bloody face
and rump. Then the grey crows came, and picked out the
eyes, and the lashless eyelids drooped grotesquely over
empty sockets. The kits in the cairn would be restless with
hunger.

In the sun-glare of evening the men came down from the hill
to seek Damh Mor in his hollow. But the calf was no longer
there.

"Och, she will have moved him," said Stewart; "but she
won't be far. This iss her ground and she'll hardly move him
yet."

He climbed on to a boulder for a view, and scanned the slope
below. In a few minutes he had made out five calves with his
naked eye; then, far down, and to the right, he saw what looked
like another. He unslung his glass and spied them all.

"I can see the calvie, Donald, away down on the right there.
He's on our way so we'll take a look at him."

They walked down quietly on to him, where he lay among

crowberry and bell heather in the lee of a bank. He was lying chin to ground and the peat on his flank was flaking. His sides were heaving gently with his breathing. Nearby, his mother showed herself, then ran above the men, anxious for her calf.

"And how iss the manny now?" Stewart greeted the calf. But Damh Mor struggled to his feet at the approach of the man and sprackled away gawkily to join his mother.

"Och, well," said Stewart, "we've made a job of him all right. He iss not liking the idea of meeting us again. He iss a good calf too, and should be a likely beast when his time comes."

Many calves were born on the green flats in Glen Eilid that summer, and soon Damh Mor was playing with others of his age under the watchful eyes of the hinds. Red hinds are sociable creatures, with a strong sense of social unity and deep feelings of motherhood; so, when the calves are at play, leaping and chasing, each mother keeps a watchful eye on the others as well as her own. Thus it was possible for every mother to graze out a little distance, leaving her calf in the care of other hinds for a time.

By the middle of June there were twenty-three hinds in the herd—fifteen of them with calves at foot. Damh Mor's mother was the leader, by virtue of age and wisdom. When she stood alerted, with ears up, as when an eagle flew over low or the scent of fox or man came to her on the wind, the others copied her pose. She was the last to lower her head after the threat of danger. And when she broke away, to watch from a higher ridge, the herd followed her at once without hesitation or question. Many of the hinds were her daughters and grand-daughters, and often they licked her coat so that it was glossier than any.

In those days, Damh Mor's mother was tireless in her mothering of him. She licked him till his coat was glossed and silked, and the spots as flawlessly white as new-fallen snow. Running with her daily, up and down and along the green-terraced slope, he soon learned every contour on his limited range; and when his mother stopped suddenly, with nostrils flared to the wind, he pressed close against her flank, sensing danger without trying to understand the nature of it.

One day he was playing with a small hind calf in a corrie when he saw a dark-coated hind standing by herself under a rock where woodrush grew. She was standing with her head down, and her ears drooped, making low noises in her throat. The calves frolicked up to her and, with necks stretched, reached out to smell her. She sniffed them over gently in return, nuzzled them, then walked to where her own little one was lying. The calves followed her, and when they saw him in the heather they tapped him with a forehoof, bidding him rise and play. But he could not rise, for he was dead. Still-born, his eyes had never opened to see the mountains and sky; his ears had never hearkened to the song of the wild waters. The hind patted him with a hoof, and a soft sob came from her throat.

The calves ran back to their mothers, shaking their heads against the flies; but the bereaved hind stayed with her own. For two days she stayed with him—grazing, cudding, sleeping —then, realising he was not to be given to her, she came back to the herd and forgot her loss by lavishing her affection on the calves of others. That same day the hen eagle flew down to the dead calf, and with her sickle beak tore at the body till she had the hindquarters separated from the trunk. Spreading her vast wings, she swooshed up and away with the puny haunch grasped firmly in her great yellow talons. Within the hour she was back for the remainder, and carried it away to feed her two voracious, dark-feathered eaglets in the nest. And nothing was left of the calf except some shreds of skin, and tufts of hair, and dark blood splashes clotted on the heather.

Flies began to trouble the deer—buzzing, rasping or silent according to their breed—and the old hind led the herd to higher ground. Other groups of hinds were moving up, too, many with spotted calves following, and soon they were gathered on the ridges, and knolls, and high flats, seeking the windswept places to escape the tormenting flies. Few stags moved up with them, for this was hind ground, and the mature sexes of the red deer mix only fortuitously outside the season of mating. Across the glen, at still greater heights, herds of big

stags were moving, their velveted antlers like little tree plant-
ings where they crowded on the knolls.

On the high ground the grass was sweet and rain-washed
and the deer summered well. Damh Mor, great in stature at
birth, outstripped his fellows in growth on the green alpine
meadowlands. Those were halcyon days for the hinds; they
grew fat. Then the quiet of the forest was rudely broken.

Damh Mor had seen many men since that first day in the
hollow when he had been touched by human hands: shepherds
with their dogs, the stalker with glass and terriers, climbers on
the mountain. But his mother had never been alarmed, so the
calf was not afraid. She knew, from her long experience, that
men were not to be feared at that time of year; just as she knew
the difference between the shepherd with his dogs and a man
with a rifle. Then in early autumn, when his spots were fading,
the calf began to see men daily—men in parties, with ponies
and dogs and guns. The first gunshots alarmed him, and he had
an urge to panic, till the sight of his mother, alert but unafraid,
reassured him. Again she knew that the shooting was not her
concern. Her calf saw the grouse coveys hurtling across the
glen, but did not understand.

The grouse-shooting parties ceased to come and, for a few
brief days, the quiet times returned. The calves played on the
high flats where the ptarmigan were flying. Roving bands of
stags, passing over the ground, had antlers clear of velvet.
Flocks of ravens began to fly in. The hard smack of a heavy-
calibre rifle echoed in the glen, and became a familiar sound in
the following days. The calf heard, and looked at his mother.

Almost daily he saw two men entering the glen, and climbing on the far side, stalking into the stag ranges. Often, there
was rifle fire later. But he ceased to listen; it was remote from
his life, and he was not afraid. That was until the band of
seven stags, with a fine ten-pointer among them, came to join
the hinds on the flats of Ben Dearg. Soon afterwards he
learned.

The sky was clouded dark that morning, and the white mists
were sweeping. Damh Mor was lying near his mother, who was
irritable. Every now and again she would jump to her feet and

face the wind with wagging ears and shrewd nostrils. The calf watched her running up and down, not understanding. But on one of her uneasy runs she found cause for her vague fears. She heard the sound at her back; it was the scrape of a boot on rock, and she knew it. Without hesitation or haste she trotted away, with calves, hinds and stags herding in behind her.

She came to a halt on a horse-shoe ridge, with the ground falling away steeply in scree on the outside of the curve. For some time she stood facing her back trail, with ears up and nostrils flared; there was no movement on the flat. She lay down, with Damh Mor beside her. But not for long.

Suddenly she was on her feet again, facing the wind, with nostrils twitching in question. No scent came to her, but still she stood, with ears up and muzzle high. Hinds and stags lifted heads to stare where she was staring, then one by one lowered muzzles to grass again. Still the mother of Damh Mor stood: taut, motionless, nostrils sifting. Ten minutes—fifteen— she was lowering her head; the movement caught her eye; the head shot up again. She could not place it, that fleeting movement. So she held her pose, staring, watching.

The ten-pointer crossed in front of her. Her eyes did not follow him. He walked to the spine of the ridge, splayed his legs, reached down to grass. . . .

The whiplash crack of the rifle brought the hinds milling behind her, while the stags threw up their heads. The ten-pointer leaped forward with muzzle up, open-mouthed, and crashed down the scree. Damh Mor ran to the ridge-edge with his mother. The stag was bouncing and rolling down the scree, with legs sprawling, loosening stones as he fell. Near the bottom the body slithered to a stop, cut and battered, with one antler broken. And Stewart was rising from behind a grey rock with a companion, looking down where the ten-pointer had fallen. The mother of Damh Mor cantered from the ridge, changed direction, and ran uphill and upwind, with the herd bunched behind her. Not till she had reached a commanding viewpoint high above did she stop to look back at the men.

Thus was Damh Mor introduced to the power of man and the modern rifle, probably without realising that the two things were related to each other or the death leap of the ten-pointer stag. It was his only experience that season, for the stag group went its way—they were rags anyway, Stewart had said after spying them, and not worth the stalking—and no rifle was fired on the hind ground of Ben Dearg again. The calf forgot quickly. He grazed and sucked and grew, heedless of the days, now garbed like his mother, happy and carefree under her watchful eyes. The golden plovers left the high ground; the ptarmigan stayed. And ravens gorged on huge grallochs in the quiet places where proud stags had been grassed.

Damh Mor followed his mother down with the herd when the night frosts were keen and the first snows whitened the tops. Clear, vitreous blue were the day skies, with the wind snell from the north; at night the peaks were etched, indigo and glowing purple, against fiery sunsets. The peat hags, brimmed, were pools of crimson fire on the shadowy levels. And when the moon rose, frosty-brilliant, the hills were a spectral wonderland, mirrored dark on silvered waters.

Big stags came striding down from the high ground—maned, swollen of neck, burning with the fever of the rut—to wallow in the hags and emerge like primeval monsters, while Orion glittered in the south-sky and the Aurora flickered with blue and amethyst flame. The big stags ripped the heather with their antlers, and the glen was filled with their roaring. They rushed this way and that, vapouring, gathering hinds, and the smell of them was heavy on the air.

Twenty-three hinds with fifteen calves, including Damh Mor and his mother, were rounded up by a big switch-horn stag with grey face and leonine mane. All night he herded his harem, drinking much and eating not at all, running here and there and yonder, challenging, driving off lesser beasts trying to raid, and always roaring. Up and down the glen, and on the terraced slopes, other stags were grunting, gasping, and belling. Damh Mor, bewildered, held close to his mother's flank; the other calves, too, were clinging to their dams. The hinds behaved casually, allowing the switch to herd them; but they were cool, even indifferent, and grazed and rested while he challenged and postured and wore himself out to hold them.

The switch held his herd for ten days, after which he was blown and lean, with tucked-up belly. At dusk a tall ten-pointer strode into the territory: bold, strong, newly come to the rut. At once the switch ran to meet him. The ten-pointer halted, with hindlegs braced and rump down, presenting a bold front; they roared at each other, with antlers lowered; but there was no head-on clash.

The newcomer side-stepped, seeking a flank opening. The switch moved sideways to keep him in front. They touched antlers and side-stepped again. For fifty yards they moved, sideways to the left, never engaging; they side-stepped back, still not engaging. Then the ten-pointer put down his head and charged.

Taken by surprise, or perhaps because he was worn out, the switch was thrust back—back—back—slotting and furrowing the peat. He was pushed on his haunches; he was prodded in flank; he was hustled into a hag. When he struggled out, dripping peat sludge and water, there was no more fight in him. He turned away and, spring-footed, trotted from the ground.

The old hind, who was the mother of Damh Mor, accepted the new lord as indifferently as she had accepted the switch. Being fresh from the hill he tried to keep the herd on foot, rousing them when they rested. He cut out a company of ten hinds and seven calves from another harem, and drove them to enlarge his own. With the stag calves he was friendly, but every now and again he would run out a hind calf and prod her. The old hinds then became watchful, flanking their calves when he was near and butting him smartly if he persisted in boring in to hustle them.

He was tall and beautiful, the ten-pointer; but his fine head was the death of him. . . .

He was roaring and pawing when Damh Mor's mother swivelled her head and leaped away. Instantly, her own followers and the new hinds surged after her. Damh Mor ran in her slots, a little calf playing second in command. For a moment the ten-pointer stood still watching them; clearly he did not know what had set them off. They were running fast, and climbing. He had either to follow them or lose them.

Already two younger stags were cutting in to head them. But even as he moved the rifle spoke, and when he did run after them he was running a race against death. Blood was oozing from him; the world was reeling. Among bog myrtle he fell, and rolled on his side. He was dead.

Again Damh Mor saw two men rising and walking to where the dead ten-pointer lay. They bent over him. Damh Mor did not know what they were doing, but the sickly smell of blood came to him on the wind. The men dragged the body to a deer path and left it there. Later, two others came with a garron and slung the ten-pointer over the saddle; then the pony was led away. The old hind avoided the spot where the big stag had fallen; his gralloch was there and the smell offended her. Damh Mor saw the ravens flying down to it at first light the next morning, and heard the croaking as they feasted.

So the herd was split between two younger stags, fifteen to one and eighteen to the other; but five came back from the smaller group under cover of darkness and the twenty-three clannish hinds of Damh Mor's group were together again. When the rut was over they followed the old hind to her favourite ground, and their old life was restored.

Damh Mor suckled his mother till the nights were long as two daylights, and the late milk prepared him for the winter's rigour. The rains came, chill and drenching, then the snow in wild storms from the north. Soon it lay drifted in the glens, and the deer came down in great herds to scrape for grass. Many calves died, to feed raven and fox and crow; but Damh Mor lived because he was forward for his age and there was great strength in him.

Of all our wild animals the red deer has the longest childhood; he grows quickly, but matures slowly. As a yearling the calf will still follow his mother, even when she has a new spotted offspring. At three he may still be running with the hinds—immature, a knobber with the veriest buds of antlers, unstirred yet by the magic fire of October—but experiencing a strange urge to leave them and join the stags on their own ground.

Among deer, the knobber is a growing boy; but still a boy.

In the forests, where there is an ethic in the sport of deer-stalking, he is not considered shootable, although he may be killed in mistake for a hind. So in the stalking season (when stags are grassed for their heads), and in the hind-shooting season (when yeld hinds, without calf at foot, are killed for food), the knobber is safe. And, since man himself is now the only enemy he has to fear, he will live and grow unless cut short by accident or famine.

The knobber rising three becomes a brocket when his new antlers grow, and he is a stag at six; but at six his antlers will still be light—a promise of things to come. He may grow to be a switch; or just a rag; or a royal with brow, bay, tray and three-point top. He will, if he has never grown antlers, be a hummel, and as such will grow into a heavy, powerful beast unloved by men.

When first he takes the rut it will be as a flanker, a skirmisher, a raider of harems, a cutter-out of straggling hinds. Only when the days of roaring are far gone will he take possession, playing the master, and rutting the last hinds of the season.

Damh Mor's mother was shot yeld in his second winter and, perhaps because the ties were broken, he wandered off in his third summer and joined a company of big stags with antlers in velvet. The company began to break up when the mature stags, in full pride of antlers and with necks maned and swollen, left one by one to take the rut. Only Damh Mor and other young staggies remained. But one by one the master stags came back again, drawn-up and rib-taut, almost dead on their feet, seeking seclusion to regain their strength. While they grazed and rested Damh Mor looked out for them; he became their eyes and ears; and he became one of them.

On a blustery autumn morning five years later nine harts were feeding in a small grassy corrie on the south face of Ben Dearg. They were dark with many soakings and the peat glaur was blistering between their cletts. The biggest stag, grazing higher than his fellows, was an eight-pointer with wide-spreading antlers; he had a right-angled ear cut and three white-haired lines on his left flank. The hair had grown white on the claw-marks made by a wildcat.

D

At half-past ten in the morning the sun broke through the clouds, and its golden light filtered down through the crawling mists in the glen. Tawny and purple were the low ridges in the shimmering haze. Two miles down, from between the green forests of spruce crowding the slopes, a green shooting-brake appeared, grinding in second gear along the rough forest road. Damh Mor saw the brake far below, and watched it; but when it disappeared from sight he went back to cropping leaves of crowberry. He was fat and his antlers were hard.

Presently he lay down to chew cud. Three others lay down beside him; the rest grazed on, keeping close. They were on the terrace for the day. The wind blustered, but they were sheltered. Ptarmigan called. Damh Mor wagged his ears and chewed.

Five hundred yards away, to the right, two men were lying behind a flat boulder on a knoll, spying the stags. They had walked two miles since leaving the shooting-brake, having spied the herd from the road. Fergus Stewart had his glass on the stags, examining their heads.

"There's one or two likely beasts there," he said over his shoulder. "We'll get into them when yon hind moves out of sight."

"Would she not move anyway, Fergus, if she saw us?" asked the other. He was young, a schoolboy, the tenant's son out for his first stag and the first stag of the season.

"Och, she would move sure enough, Chawn my boy, and likely take every beast on this side away with her. Look! She's going now!"

The stalker slapped his glass shut, cased it and slung it. "Now, Chawn," he instructed, "you will keep behind me please, and do as I tell you."

They bent double as they left the knoll, and did not straighten up till the contours hid them from the stags on the terrace. Moving without haste, they walked upright to the breast of a rise less than two hundred yards from the deer. There Stewart bellied down and wriggled to the top. Unslinging the glass, he spied each beast in turn, then back-crawled to tell young John what he was seeing.

"There iss good heads there," he said; "a ten-pointer, a nine and an eight. We'll stalk in and try for the ten. I ken the eight-pointer because I lug-marked him—oh—let me see—eight years ago. He's got white on his ribs where he was sair scarted by a cat as a calf."

"A cat?"

"Yes, Chawn my boy; a big wildcat—a real teuchter of a beast that hurted him sairly."

"Why don't we go for him instead then?" John said. "A head with such a story! Fergus, what a first stag that would be!"

"Och, yes, indeed," the stalker answered frowning. "I'm sure you would be gran pleased with him. But if you wass to wait until he was a royal now it would be a better story entirely. He has all the makings of a great stag. But we'll see. . . ."

The ground between the low ridge and the terrace was open, and Stewart surveyed with a critical eye before going in to the final stalk.

"Chawn my boy," he said; "this iss going to be tricky. There iss next to no cover at all, so keep close and watch me."

Stewart walked at a crouch to the end of the ridge and there raised his eyes. No stag was looking in their direction. Getting down on his stomach he elbowed his way through waving grass, with his eyes fixed on the deer. John followed, with his face almost against the stalker's boots.

The cover thinned, and the stalker whispered: "Easy now!" A stag turned his head, casually. Stewart froze. John froze. The stag turned his head away. Man and boy elbowed forward again. The last fifty yards were nerve-racking for the boy. They crawled and froze; they wriggled a yard then had to lie face down, sometimes for many minutes till a stag looked away. But at last they were in a wet hollow, with heather on top, where they could sit. They were now sixty-five yards from the unwarned stags.

Stewart parted heather warily with his hands and looked through at the stags. Six were lying; three were on foot, with muzzles to grass. The best stags were down.

"They're still lying, Chawn," he said, "so content yourself and get the shakes out of you. You don't want to be missing."

"How long will it be before they rise?" John asked.

"Och, they might stay like that for a gey while. We'll see. If they take too long we can maybe coax them up."

The stalker lay on his stomach in the hollow, watching through the heather screen and getting his shirt and trousers stained and wet with peat. Fifteen minutes passed before the first stag rose. It was the ten-pointer.

"Chawn!" whispered Stewart. "The ten-pointer iss up, and broadside. Maybe you should take him. There iss no saying what might happen if we wait too long."

John, still thinking of the stag with the marks of the wildcat, looked through the heather; but when he saw the ten-pointer out in front he reached for the rifle. Stewart rolled aside, letting the boy into his place. John poked the rifle through. The stalker held the heather with one hand; the other was on the boy's shoulder.

"Wait now," the stalker said. "Now, easy does it, Chawn my boy. Right! You can take him now, sir!"

No stag was ever killed cleaner. The ten-pointer leaped, ran a tight half-circle and rolled on his side. Damh Mor and the rest of the herd ran twenty yards and bunched. Then they stopped and looked back, with heads high, sifting the wind and smelling nothing. Only when the boy rose to run to his stag did they break away to the higher ground, far out of rifle range.

From a heathery knowe Damh Mor watched them at the gralloch, all unaware that his life had been spared by the whim and cunning of a stalker, who knew that a fine head in the sights can be made more tempting than a lesser head with a story.

The autumn was wet and smoorey and the big stags came late to the rut. Damh Mor was running with seven full harts and a following of six staggies and knobbers, feeding and lying in the highest corrie of Ben Dearg. He had grown a mane; his neck was swelling; he was irritable. One day the fire burned in him and he grew quarrelsome, eating little. The next night, at darkening, he strode away from the group and made his way down to the glen.

Down in the hind ground he heralded his entry by loud roaring and coughing and choking grunts. On the slopes and in the glen other stags were belling. Damh Mor began to run at a stiff-legged trot, stopping every fifty yards to bellow and rip heather with his antlers. At a shallow peaty pool he lay down to wallow; he rolled on one side then the other, squirming into the mire on his shoulder and gouging the wet peat with his antler tips. When he rose he was plastered with glaur, dark and dripping, snorting steamy breath, a fearsome apparition— a king stag in his prime.

Up and down the levels were many harems of hinds with big stags in possession. Damh Mor ran a wide circuit in the glen, skirting groups large and small, till he found a herd of thirteen hinds on a flat by the river, in charge of a young stag with short, puny horns. The young stag roared and strode out to challenge. Damh Mor roared back at him, and trotted boldly on to the flat.

Serious fights between red stags are uncommon; mostly they are formalised encounters of great punctilio and bluster. Sometimes they are long-drawn-out, with stags pushing head to head, and sometimes there is much fury. Occasionally a stag is injured slightly; less frequently the injury is serious. Deaths are rare. When stags are unevenly matched the engagement is usually brief. And so it was with Damh Mor.

He met the lighter beast head to head, and pushed, slashing the peat with his hooves. The young stag had to give ground at once. He back-tracked, almost hunkering, and Damh Mor lunged past him for a flank stab. When the young beast felt the dirks scoring his ribs he broke off the engagement and ran. And Damh Mor followed him, prodding, to the edge of the territory.

Damh Mor trotted round the thirteen hinds, herding them, then strode out on to the flat, where he stretched his neck and roared. The nearest stag was three hundred yards away, so there was no direct challenge. Damh Mor roared again, turned back to his hinds, and put nose to grass. There were few stags travelling.

Eighteen hinds, many of them with calves, came walking along a deer path on the river bank when day was breaking. They turned off to skirt the flat but Damh Mor saw them and ran out to herd them. He gathered them as a collie gathers sheep and drove them on to the flat. When a hind ran out he cut wider to turn her. He held the herd all that day, when no stags were moving. By nightfall he had added five more to his harem; they had wandered out from the group held by his nearest neighbour. On the third day he was holding fifty-two hinds, and being kept constantly running to hold them against other stags coming in for the rut.

On the fourth day, at darkening and in smirring rain, he met the big royal.

The royal came to the edge of the flat and roared. Spring-footed, Damh Mor trotted out to meet him. They challenged at a range of ten yards, with muzzles raised and antlers lying back over withers; they roared at each other for four minutes, pawing forward but not moving. Then they began to side-step. They side-stepped, twenty feet apart, round half the perimeter of the flat. The royal was still outside the territory. Damh Mor, grunting, turned away. And the royal rushed at him.

But Damh Mor was alert. He was half-way round when the assault came, so was taken in flank instead of between the thighs. The blow winded him, but it also stung him to terrible rage. He engaged the big royal antler to antler. With hindlegs splayed, and rumps down, they buckled and pushed; they spun in circles, slashing the peat; they bored and grunted, with every muscle strained, but neither could start the other moving. In a tight group, fifty-two hinds stood watching.

Both beasts began to tire. They stopped straining. They tried to lift their heads, but could not; they tried to disengage, but could not; their antlers were locked. They pulled and twisted and pushed, far into the night, but the branching antlers were inextricably locked. At last the royal fell, exhausted, pulling Damh Mor down with him. They lay on their sides, skull to skull, with flanks heaving, bleared and snorting vapour, helpless, fallen at the peak of their power to die the long slow death of starvation.

The locked stags ate the ground bare where they lay; then hunger came to torment them. After many days they grew weak, and moved little, and the grey crows came to look at them. The royal was under the greater strain, due to the manner of the locking; his head was always clear of the ground. He lost strength rapidly; his senses dulled more quickly. When his tongue was showing out of the side of his mouth the crows flew down and pecked at it. He kicked feebly, and they flapped up and away; but they came back soon to peck again. They pulled pieces from his tongue; then they picked out an eye.

Damh Mor saved himself that day from the fate of the emaciated and dying royal. Each time a crow touched his head he kicked out with a forehoof and frightened it away. The grey birds perched on an antler and peered at him. But during the daylight he watched out for them, and kept them away with a foot. At night they did not come.

Next morning there were six crows ground-hopping around the helpless stags. They took more of the royal's tongue; Damh Mor's hoof still dabbed at them, keeping them away; but they would have had him in the end if no help had come. Help came at last in the form of the red deer's only enemy—Man!

Stewart, going out with the under-keeper along a ridge of Ben Dearg, saw the crows gathered on the flat beside the river, and wondered what they were at. He drew his glass and spied them carefully, and the locked stags loomed large in the object lens.

"There iss two stags down there, Donald," he said. "They're on their sides by God, and the hoodies are at them. We had better take a look."

The hoodies took wing long before the men reached the flat. Damh Mor tried to struggle up when he saw the men beside him, but he was too weak. Stewart approached cautiously, not knowing how much fight was left in the stags till he saw the condition of the royal. Then he swore.

"This iss the first time I've seen anything like this in thirty years, Donald. They've been like this for days, man, as sure's a goat iss a hairy beast! Look at them: a royal with half his tongue away, and the buggers have picked out his eye."

"They're finished," Donald said.

"This other one has more left in him though. And man . . . yes! Yes! Man Donald, it is! It's the stag I lug-marked in Glen Eilid man! He's lying on the side with the white hairs."

"Maybe we should shoot both of them, eh?" Donald was pessimistic. "There's not much of them now."

Stewart put a ·22 bullet into the empty eye-socket of the royal. The stricken beast shuddered only a little and lay still. Blood began to ooze from the hole.

"No, Donald!" Stewart decided; "we'll let the marked stag have his chance. Let's see can we separate them."

But they could not. They tried to manœuvre the dead weight of the royal to twist clear the locked tines, but they were too firmly held. Stewart shook his head.

"We'll need a saw, Donald. It's useless to try further and the big stag might strike with a foot. I'll go on to the top if you get down quick to the foresters for a saw. You should be back in a bit more than an hour. I'll spy you coming and come down."

An hour and a half later the men were back with a saw. Stewart started sawing on one of the royal's antlers, close to the coronet. "We might as well take them off the dead one," he remarked. In a few minutes Damh Mor was free, for when the royal's antlers were loose the men had little difficulty in extricating them.

"We'll go away a bitty and see how he makes out," Stewart said. And they left, taking the antlers of the royal with them.

Damh Mor moved his head, and discovered he was no longer held. He shook himself and rolled over on his back; then he fell on his side, panting with the exertion. He tried to rise, and fell; he rose and stumbled. He fell again, with his muzzle in cool, waving grass. He lipped the grass and began to eat, lying on his side. When there was nothing left to bite within reach, he rolled over and found more grass. He continued eating.

When Stewart spied him the next day he was still down. But he was twenty yards away from the spot where he had lain the day before—and eating.

"He'll make out," the stalker said to himself, and went on his way.

The days of roaring were not yet over, but Damh Mor was a sick stag; there was no fire left in him. He was gaunt and tucked-up, and walked with his head low. His neck was stiff, causing him pain; his loins ached; and he had to lie down frequently when grazing. He craved a quiet place to rest. So one day, with a little knobber for company, he hirpled to a high terrace on Ben Dearg where no deer were lying, and there found the seclusion he longed for.

But winter followed close on the rut that year, and in a day the high ridges were white. The sudden change drove Damh Mor down to the lower corries and terraces, for he was weaker yet than any of the big stags run out by the rut. With him came the knobber, who was alert and fat.

The next storm blanketed the hills, and a glassy wind from the north drifted the snow in the glens. The deer stood out the blizzard on wind-swept ridges, and gathered there on the blue, sunny days when its fury was spent. At darkening, they filed down to the river flats, where they scraped through the snow, and when they cleared a circular patch they ate the grass right into the ground. All along the river the snow was stained with urine and droppings, and the white slopes were veined with trails slashed by the hooves of deer.

Damh Mor came down and stayed down. He found a break in the deer fence where the wires had sagged under the weight of snow, and leaped over into the lofty, spacious shelter of the pine forest. The knobber ploughed over on his heels. There were other stags in the wood, and Damh Mor joined up with them. The grazing was good, so he became a woodland stag.

The deer soon found where hay was being put down for out-wintering garrons, and went down to the timber road to fill their paunches. The shaggy, sturdy ponies laid back their ears at the deer, and kicked at them. But the deer snatched rips, eating as they moved. Damh Mor lowered his head in threat, and the garrons kept away from him.

During his wanderings in the wood he found a way out by a narrow bridge over the river. One night he crossed it and followed the winding timber road down into the glen farm-lands, with the knobber and six stags following. That night they cropped grass among blackface sheep, and found turnips which they flaked with their teeth. Damh Mor returned to the wood in the morning, but at night he went back again, and this time he was leading nine stags and the knobber. Thus a stag teaches bad habits to his fellows.

When the snow was hock deep, a herd of sixteen stags and staggies was pillaging the low ground at night and lying up in

the wood during the day. They escaped punishment until they
slashed with their hooves into the potato pit and paunched
on Golden Wonders. There was frost in the night and many
potatoes were spoiled. The next day at dusk the farmer and his
men were waiting for them.

A fusillade of shot greeted them as they approached the pit
—three twelve-bores and a ·303 Lee-Enfield rifle. A big switch
went down, killed clean; the knobber swerved back trailing a
hindleg crippled by No. 3 shot; one other stag lurched about
drunkenly, hit full in the brisket. Damh Mor broke back with
the rest of the herd, with a few pellets in his haunch. The
knobber hobbled after them, but the wounded stag was
dropped by a bullet from the Lee-Enfield rifle. Then they were
being hounded by a huge dog—part deerhound, part collie—
who tried to cut out the crippled knobber.

Damh Mor halted, vapouring, when he was well into the
wood. The other stags passed him, then turned, crowding at
his back. The knobber was less than twenty yards away when
the dog pulled him down, tearing out his throat. The smell of
blood, the stinging pain in his haunch, and the sight of the dog
kindled a terrible, and strange, fury in the heart of Damh Mor.
With a grunt he bore down on the dog.

The hound was fast, and cunning, but he was taken completely by surprise by the impetuous assault of the stag. He
leaped for a hold, baring his tremendous teeth. Damh Mor
turned away, then hooked back his head, and an antler took
the hound in the belly. He yelped, and fell, and his blood
dripped black on the snow. Damh Mor drew back, snorting;
his fury was spent. The dog was limping away, whimpering.
The deer watched him out of sight, then turned away into the
darkness of the pine forest.

They were pawing snow under the trees, seeking grass, when
the dog was lying on the kitchen table at the farm, having nine
stitches put in his belly by a veterinary surgeon.

In his eleventh year Damh Mor took the rut as a royal. His
antlers were wide and symmetrical: brow, bay, tray, and
three-point top forming a deep cup. He had as fine a head as
any beast ever seen on the forest, and was spared to carry it to

the rut because the stalker had a Nelson eye when it pleased him.

That year he rutted thirty-five hinds before he was thrown and battered by a big hummel—a hornless stag, the real master of the deer forest—who hit him with head and forefeet: twenty-two stone of uncrowned bone and muscle toppling the finest head in the forest. After his defeat, Damh Mor retired to the lonely corrie high on Ben Dearg, where he joined up with two other run-out stags and a tawny-faced knobber who might have been his son.

The high tops were white-capped early, but only a thin tracking snow covered the slopes at the end of the year. The hind groups held to the high ridges, where the feed was still good, and during the shooting season Damh Mor and his trio often ran with them. Stewart, spying for good yeld hinds, saw Damh Mor frequently, recognising him by his ear mark and the white hairs on his flank.

"There iss the big royal again," he would say to Donald. "He should have left some good calves behind him whateffer."

The real winter set in early in the new year, with blizzard mounting on blizzard till only the crag faces showed black on the hills. The deer trekked down in hundreds, vapouring, churning up the snow in clouds: dark wraiths in the swirling chaos. With them came the hares of the mountains, in droves; flitting, leaping; ghostly shapes, white-furred, on snow-shoe feet. Foxes, gaunt and hungry, followed the hares. All living things deserted the tops: even the white ptarmigan, who live on the roof of the world.

Week after week the snow lay deep, always the tracks of fox and deer, hare and rabbit and wildcat were being covered by fresh blizzards, and everywhere there was ice—sheeting and ribbing the rocks; in great gleaming teeth, down-pointing, along the banks of the river; columned and pillared in the corries where the frost-smoke drifted.

The deer herds blackened the river flats, and scraped them bare; but still the famine pinched them. Calves died; then the weakly stags; then the poorest hinds. Ravens and buzzards and crows flocked to the carcases. Damh Mor's ribs were showing, and his hair was lustreless. In the end, the herds left the ground. They crossed the shoulder of Ben Dearg in files half a mile long; they filed in clouds of snow down the opposite steep; they crossed the next glen, climbed to the ridge, and floundered over a vast high plateau to the low slopes beside the main motor highway—ten miles by their tracks from their usual range.

Down there they were sheltered from the worst scourging of winds and snow-storms, but other perils soon came to face them. Damh Mor, scraping for grass on the levels, saw a snow-plough clearing the road, followed by cars and lorries, and raced in terror to the slopes with a herd of fifty stags. All day they watched the traffic grinding slowly along the frozen highway, and at night they came down to feed. But, though they pawed in the snow all night, they were still hungry in the morning. So they continued feeding throughout the day and, becoming accustomed to traffic, they lost their fear of it.

On a night of brilliant, unclouded moonlight Damh Mor was feeding near the icy road in a mixed group of stags, hinds and calves, when he saw the headlamps of an approaching car. Beyond standing with head up, to stare, he paid no attention to it, for he had lost fear. He heard the racing of the engine, the crunch of tyres on frozen snow, then suddenly he was caught in a blinding spotlight swivelling on the roof.

Four men came out of the car—two with Service rifles, one with a Sten gun, and one with a smooth-bore firing ball cartridges. With a fifth man arcing the spotlight the four began to pour a deadly fire into the massed herd of deer. Bullets whined and cracked; the smooth-bore blasted; rat-tat-tat went the Sten gun. Deer leaped and fell; deer broke away; calves bleated. The herd milled. Damh Mor, unhit, broke away in a circle, with hinds and stags following.

He crossed the road and halted, to look back. The spotlight switched, and again the bullets ploughed the snow or wupped into the bodies of starving deer. Beasts fell; beasts limped; a hind, with her gut trailing, hirpled along the road with her bleating calf at her flank. In a bloody perimeter the dark shapes of deer were lying, kicking in the snow. This time, Damh Mor left the dangerous proximity of the road and ploughed uphill out of range and out of sight, with hinds and stags crowding behind.

A lorry followed the car, with dipped lights, and stopped to load on the deer lying along the road. Then it moved on, and the watching deer heard more shooting down the glen. In the morning, the snow on the road was red-splashed for miles with the blood of deer, and their grallochs were strewn along the verge. During the day, stalkers and keepers tramped the flats, killing the dying and tracking down the wounded. And they had to shoot many bleating calves standing over dead hinds who were their mothers.

More raids were made on the lean herds after that night, but Damh Mor had learned much, and when he saw headlamps approaching in the dark he bounded away from the road. When the thaw broke he stayed away from the road altogether until he was fit to travel the hard way home.

It was into March before the deer began the long trek back to their own range, for the deep snow on the slopes shrank slowly in the thaw. When dark ridges and hummocks at last began to show, the snow fell in masses into the mountain burns, which became boiling, raging torrents. Every ditch became a burn, and the rivers rose, overflowing their banks and inundating the levels.

Damh Mor, still lean and ribbed, started back in daylight with a small company of stags: though he was not waywise on these slopes he set his course unerringly for home. They travelled slowly that first day, stopping for long periods to bite the cold, snow-washed grass. Towards nightfall they were joined by a big herd of hinds, with calves and staggies, and they travelled with them to the plateau during the darkness. In daylight they grazed and walked over the snow-patchy plateau, then stopped; the glen slopes and the distant face of Ben Dearg were still blanketed in white.

On the high flat, and along the top of the glen, lay many dead deer and clean-picked skeletons. The stench from the carcases was heavy on the air, and Damh Mor avoided the places where they were lying. Foxes came to feed on the carrion on that lonely height, and in the raw, windy daylight flocks of ravens and crows flew down to join them. Of such are the scavengers of the hills.

Heavy rain began to fall, and the deer left the top to cud and sleep on the slopes. They fed wet and slept wet, but the rain hastened the melting of the snows, and soon the dark slopes of Ben Dearg were showing. The hinds began to file down into the glen, and Damh Mor followed with the other stags.

The river was a white-crested, rioting torrent and the roar of it filled the glen. The leading hind turned downstream at the bank, and found a flat, pebbly stretch where the water raced clear and glassy smooth. She plunged in and high-stepped across, splashing the water to her ears while the strong current pulled at her legs. Behind her, the herd crashed in, ten abreast, and the water boiled as they crossed. A weakling calf fell *ba-aing*, and was rolled away by the rushing water. His mother splashed after him, trying to strike him up, but he was tossed where the water surged between boulders, and lost in the seething pool beyond. A dozen hinds, with calves at foot, turned back from the river, fearful of the crossing.

Damh Mor breasted the next ridge, dripping. Ahead was the age-old track he knew. The path led across a wild stretch of steep scree, with snow-capped crags rearing high above. On the hard, naked rocks of the scree was the shadowy track, trodden by the hooves of countless generations of deer. The herd was strung out across it, nose to tail, when the avalanche fell on them.

They heard the warning rumble and looked up. The leading beasts, Damh Mor among them, broke into a run on the treacherous scree. Above, the entire snowy crest of the crag seemed to leap out and fall asunder. For a moment it seemed to hang, a stupendous mass of disintegrating snow: then it descended. The thunder of it drowned the thunder of the torrents. Boulders and spinning cornices of snow hurtled far out over the glen. The main mass rumbled down the scree in a cloud of white, carrying rocks and heather and uprooted saplings irresistibly before it. It struck the centre of the line of deer and engulfed them; it tossed others down the scree, with legs wildly flying, and they were pounded, and battered, and broken. When the snow-cloud cleared there was a fifty-yard gap in the line of deer.

Damh Mor, with the leading hinds, did not stop running till he was on the lowest ridge of Ben Dearg. When he stopped his tongue was showing, and his breathing was laboured. Not since the day of the wildcat's attack had he known such panic terror.

In soft April weather he cast his antlers in the heather on Ben Dearg, and for some days the raw sores irked him. But, presently, the buds of his new antlers appeared and the long, draining process of growth began all over again.

In the first weeks he lived high on Ben Dearg, growing fat, but at the height of summer he moved higher still, right to the lofty wind-swept top where there were no flies to irk him. There he found other big stags grazing and he settled down with them in easy-going camaraderie. They quarrelled but rarely, and when they did they reared and boxed with their forehooves, being mindful of their antlers in the velvet.

Damh Mor's horns grew quickly. The velvet on them was warm and furry, and he took care not to injure it. Sometimes he would rub gently against a stone; and sometimes he would pass a hindhoof between the coronets and scratch cannily the velveted shaft; but he was ever careful not to abuse them.

By August he was again carrying his royal head: twelve points—with long, evenly matched tines thick and blunt-tipped in the velvet. Soon he felt irritable, and started to rub vigorously against stones or thrash in the heather. The velvet cracked, and began to peel, and he rubbed and thrashed more vigorously than ever. Sometimes he would scrape at the fraying lappets with a hindfoot. For a time his head was in tatters; then, suddenly, he was clean, with antlers hard and dark and the long tines tipped with ivory.

Once more he was the proud royal, awaiting the hot rush of blood and the wild magic of October. The stalking season was well advanced. He was already maned-up for the days of roaring.

That Chawn who had seen Damh Mor as an eight-pointer came up for the last days of the stalking. He was a young man now, training to be an officer, and ettling to be a Gordon Highlander.

"If you're nae a Gordon you're nae a sodger," he greeted the stalker when he met him to plan their day on the hill.

"Och, yes," Stewart laughed. "That will be right enough, sir, but I was a Cameron myself."

They talked, and it came as the stalker knew it would.

"Where are you hiding the big royal, Fergus? I hear you sawed him loose last year, but father says he hasn't even seen him this year."

"Och, now," said Stewart, "it isn't that I have been hiding him at all. It iss just that he iss always somewhere else. He iss a very precarious beast, whateffer!"

"I want that head, Fergus. And you're going to take me to it. I want what the cat left this time!"

"Och, well, we shall see tomorrow. But I wass thinking now the beast might grow to be an Imperial yet. . . ."

In the morning they drove up the forest road in John's own car. The rifles were in the back, and on the seat lay a great pied hound, deep-flewed, with eyes showing the haw. He was a cross between a staghound and a pointer.

"That iss a precarious beast to be taking to the hill for the stalking, sir," Stewart remarked for the tenth time as the car lurched along the road.

"He's a good dog, Fergus. He's got staghound blood in him. I just want to see how he behaves on the hill among the deer. Down south they hunt the deer, you know, with staghounds, on horseback. . . ."

"Indeed, now! Iss it that they can't walk in yon country? A rifle iss the only proper way to kill the stag, sir!"

"I think I agree with you at that, Fergus. So here's to the big royal. I'll keep Major on the leash."

When they left the car they climbed for an hour and then spied the ground. They spent the next two hours walking the high ridges about Ben Dearg. The stalker spied every group of stags, and shook his head each time. "I think we might have lunch now," he suggested; "then we'll see. I think I ken where yon royal might be lying."

Stewart worked round the mountain, and suddenly saw the tips of stag antlers in the big corrie. Bidding John wait with the dog, he crept forward slowly to the top of a little ridge. There he spied the stags carefully. And, having spied them, he rolled on his side and waved John forward.

"Your big stag's there," he told him. "The range is about eighty yards. Would you like to take him?"

"Would I...? Let me have a look. Will you take hold of the dog, please?"

Damh Mor was standing on a little knoll scratching a shoulder with an antler tip. There were five other stags with him, standing close, but not in the way. John wriggled back and said:

"He's a beauty! I'm so excited I'll probably miss him. What kind of whisky do you drink, Fergus?"

"Och, Chawn, sir, you'd better get your beast first. As for the whisky now—a bottle of the stuff your father has will do fine!"

The stalker motioned the young man into the best position, then flattened beside him. The young man lined up the rifle. Then Damh Mor turned half round.

"Wait now!" the stalker warned. "Wait till he turns broadside! There he goes. Easy now! You can take him now, Chawn my boy!"

The young man's squeeze on the trigger was even. He fired. The stags in the corrie looked round, but none moved.

"Too low! You were too low! But they'll wait a minute yet. Try him again. But easy now. Take it easy. Now; whenever you're ready."

This time Damh Mor leaped high and vanished behind the knoll. Immediately the other stags followed. In a moment the corrie was empty.

"I missed him again!" the young man said in disgust. "I couldn't hit a battleship."

"Och, no, now! You hit him, of that I'm sure. But I don't know how sairly. I heard the strike of the bullet. We micht need that big dog o' yours yet."

They walked slowly over the broken ground to the corrie, and looked from the top of the knoll where Damh Mor had stood. There was not a single deer in sight. The big pied hound began to whimper.

"That settles it!" said John in disgust.

"Does it now?" Stewart's voice was bantering. "Well, look you here! Look at this!"

Ten yards from the spot where the great stag had stood lay a

E

steaming gralloch. "If I'm not mistaken," Stewart said, "your stag's away without his guts! Your bullet must have ripped his belly. But he can't be far away—not without that." And he nodded towards the warm paunch and entrails.

They cast about in a half-circle, looking among heather and lichened boulders, with the hound feathering ahead. But Damh Mor was not within fifty yards, or a hundred. Frowning, Stewart went back over the ground, and began to follow the blood spashes on the heather. At last he said:

"Will you slip the dog, Chawn? I can't understand this."

The hound was eager when slipped, and raced away whimpering, with muzzle brushing the heather tips. Then, with a low cry, he started to run Damh Mor's blood-line. The men watched him and, when he disappeared round a shoulder three hundred yards away, Stewart shook his head.

"What the hell . . ." he began. "The beast can't have got that far! But we'd better follow the dog and see what he's after."

Stewart strode out to the point where the dog had disappeared, and scanned the brae face with shrewd eyes; then he unslung his glass and spied the ground slowly. He could see nothing. Nor could he hear anything, for the big hound was running mute. Slapping the telescope shut, he struck out along the face, now watching the ground, following the stag by his blood splashes and the slots of his cletts on the peat.

They found the hound baying Damh Mor on a heathery knowe, more than a mile from the spot where he had been gralloched by a bullet. The big stag was swaying on his legs, with head low and antlers at the present. Blood was dripping from him, but slowly, with seconds between the drips, for he was nearly drained and his heart was white. His proud eyes had the glaze of death; they were open, but they were no longer seeing. As the men approached, Damh Mor toppled over on his side—dead.

Stewart looked at him, and frowned. For a long moment he stared at the great stag in silence. Then he turned to Chawn with a sigh:

"Och, well," he said, "he was a precarious beast whateffer, but he'll neffer be an Imperial now. . . ."

The Mousers

THE one was as fiercely whiskered as the other. In fact, four of them were fiercely whiskered, though if you'd looked closely at Spider you'd have noticed that his moustache and beard tuft were made of feathers. The cat, who should have had the most spectacular whiskers of all, had none: he lost them when the brooder lamp blew up in his face.

But perhaps I'd better begin at the beginning. And the first thing you've to understand is that this story is entirely true, and that any resemblance to living creatures is quite intentional.

Well, there was Gallacher's Nip and Gallacher's Spider, and little Johnny Whittret, with Gallacher's cat Scotch Jimmy standing by, whiskerless, crafty, aloof, with his eye on the main chance. Gallacher of Mossrigg was big and brawny, with a crop of horse-hair sprouting from the neck of his shirt. He had a lesser crop bristling from his nostrils, and the rook-purple cheeks of a twice-a-day shaver. And he had the kind of laugh you'd have expected from a horse, supposing a horse could laugh. He was as hard as Lewisian gneiss, and could shout from one county to the next. There were those, blistered at one time or another by his tongue, always ready to say he had a heart of concrete, which was not entirely true as you'll see.

Two things you'd have noticed about Gallacher right away. He wouldn't have killed a weasel for all the Tax Reliefs ever thought of, and he could tell whisky from whisky (?) blindfolded, which is no inconsiderable feat in these days. He paid great care to his 300 acres and tax on £200 a year, which is no inconsiderable feat either. He had two collies, seven cats, and as many rats as he had pullets, which put them in the Army Corps category.

Then he got the terrier.

She was so full of spirit that he called her Nip. (Before she was too big to sleep in his boot she had nipped sixteen pairs of ankles—bare, wool-clad and nylon-sheathed.) He would have called her Whisky, but he already had a cat of the name, and, as I've indicated, he hated any kind of confusion on that subject. That's why he was always good for a lecture on The Immorality of False Labelling.

His classic moan in the pub, when served with alleged mountain dew, was: "I don't know why the hell I come here and buy this stuff when I keep a hunner-gallon drum o' it at hame for the tractors."

Before Nip was old enough to need a dog licence she had the collies under her thumb. When she was old enough to need a licence she didn't have one; but she had the cats acknowledging defeat—all, that is, except Scotch Jimmy, who feared nothing but Gallacher's big Chinese gander. Then, one day, she nipped his pads when he was sitting on the horse trough, and gave him the first bath of his life. And Scotch Jimmy, dripping, bolted in ignominious defeat.

When she was full grown she could still hide behind one of Gallacher's horsehide boots—the big ones with the turned-up toes. She had a face like a vampire bat, fierce whiskers, bright eyes and wheaten hair flat and wiry. She had a heart you could not have stuffed into Gallacher's hunner-gallon drum, and a growl that won respect from every living thing, including Mussolini the boar. She had the mice on their toes. And Gallacher at her feet.

Before she came, Scotch Jimmy had been the only living thing allowed in the kitchen. He used to love it, and gloat over it; but he grew to hate it. For when Nip whisked in, Scotch Jimmy had to fume under the dresser until she whisked out again. And he resented her conquest of the citadel he had tried in vain to conquer—the spacious lap of Gallacher of Mossrigg.

They all twitted him about it, of course—the big man with the wee dog in his lap; the hard-case Gallacher mooning over a boot-high terrier who turned up her nose at good oatmeal porridge and made the collies' life a misery.

"Man, Wull," they would say, "time was when a dug wisna a dug except it wis a collie. They were jist bliddy wee yaps!"

But the man with the horsehair and the horse-laugh just guffawed and called her his boss bitch, head frog, chief puddock, and Mossrigg Führer. And Nip would lift a hindleg to let his big hand scratch her belly.

There never was a dog so fond of having her belly scratched. When Gallacher called her to pet her she lifted a hindleg and let him do his petting with his fingers on the favoured site— ventral aspect, distal end. When he returned from market she greeted him belly upwards. When she killed a rat she let him congratulate her belly. And when she slept she slept on her back, knowing his fingers would be drawn by some strange magnetism; then she could wake up and find her dreams come true.

"That's an awful belly ye ha'e!" Gallacher's wife would say six times daily. "I never did see sich a clean skin wi' sich a commandin' itch." But she played the game according to the rules and practised the same technique of limited objectives.

Nip averaged ten mice a week from the time she should have had her first licence till the time she should have had her second. That pleased Gallacher more than the thought of the fifteen shillings he didn't spend on licences. In the same period she killed three times as many rats as there were names on her pedigree. That, of course, included little pink, baby rats which she hauled from their beds and chopped as painstakingly as a man cracks a nut with his molars.

And that put her right on top of the world. When her second

spring came round she had run up a cricket score—of mice which she left like chewed string and rats that looked as if they'd been hit with a meat chopper. By then she had two lip scars and a place in Gallacher's bed. And then came Spider.

Spider arrived in Gallacher's jacket pocket, wizened and bedraggled and hungry. He had been kicked out of the nursery by two brawny sisters who cared nothing about brotherly love, to mope unheeded among the wet, cold blaeberries. After a whole day and a wet night on the ground he had almost forgotten what a mouse tasted like. He would never have remembered again if Gallacher hadn't found him or been the hard man he was.

"Anither wan for the moose brigade!" said the big man to his little wife when he produced Spider and placed him on the kitchen table.

Spider rolled down his thick eyelids while the mistress of Mossrigg exclaimed: "Good heavens! What next?" and the master went to the meal-house for mice. He didn't catch any himself; he merely picked up a couple of bodies that had been slain by Nip. And fed them to Spider.

Up till then Spider's craw was as flat as a punctured tyre, and his head sunk away down between his broad shoulders. After his second mouse he produced a neck for his head, which made him look taller, and a lump under his throat, which made him look stouter.

I should have told you that Spider was an owl, so I'll tell you now. He was a little tawny owlet who should have been white, but wasn't, because of his night in the rain. Before he ate Nip's mice—grab, gulp, grimace, chirp, grab, gulp, grimace —he was slit-eyed from hunger and fatigue; ten minutes afterwards he was round-eyed, staring with the surprised look an owl has when it's on its toes.

After the argument, Gallacher agreed with his wife that they couldn't keep an owl, so he put Spider in the barn and arranged to keep him.

The owl was put on a pile of old sacks in a corner, and given mice night and morning, and twice during the day. Nip killed the mice, and Gallacher collected them. He couldn't collect any killed by the cats, for the cats ate all their own mice and contributed nothing to the Spider fund. Scotch Jimmy, in fact, was for ever thinking up ways of making a meal of Spider.

So there was the big man, with the big feet and the big laugh, stamping into the barn each morning holding a little mouse by the tail, and calling: "Spider: Spider!" till the owlet opened his eyes and flew noiselessly down to his shoulder. After gulping the mouse, Spider would croon and chirp in his ear in the special way that tawny owls do when they're pleased, and the hard man would chuckle and scratch the bird's ear in return. He even reached the stage of trying to croon like an owl himself, and was as happy as a schoolboy when Spider answered him croon for croon.

Gallacher was a man of few words. He never put two words to work where one would do, unless in the matter of swearing, when he was inclined to be verbose and extravagant. Yet when it came to the subject of Nip or Spider he was like a father prattling about his firstborn.

Even on market days he obtruded the Mossrigg twins into the sacred domain of heifers, stirks, wedders, gilts and shotts, which shows the extent of his dotage: for dogs are seldom (unless they are collies), and owls never, subjects for conversation when the business of buying cheap and selling dear is occupying the minds of farmers. But Gallacher talked Nip and Spider in the middle of the auctioneer's chanting and over the in-between drams when the subjects should have been oats and hay. And the other hard men listened, because Gallacher was a man you listened to.

Anyway, there was Gallacher taking Nip every night to the meal store, after he'd checked the brooders and the pullets, to catch mice for an owlet he wasn't supposed to have. The terrier chopped, Gallacher grabbed, and Spider gulped, and everybody was very happy. Nip, seeing where all her mice were going, began to take an interest in the owl. She actually grew to like him, and sniffed him over when he was swallowing her mice. And Gallacher was delighted with the Mousers' Alliance, and foresaw a thin future for the rodents of Mossrigg.

The friendship of Nip and Spider lasted for three weeks,

until, in fact, the owl was making his first tentative flights and alighting on anything from the byreman's head to a cart shaft or a sow's back. It ended—the first phase anyway—when Nip saved Spider's life. And, of course, Scotch Jimmy was at the bottom of it.

No other cat bothered Spider; but then, Scotch Jimmy was like no other cat, unless you count his deceased ancestor, Satan, who was a devil. Satan died in a gin trap, but it wasn't the steel teeth that killed him. He was slain by other teeth—the teeth of a big fox called String Lug, the very fox he had mauled as a cub. That's the kind of father Scotch Jimmy had.

S.J. had his baleful eyes on Spider for two whole days while the owl was ground-skimming and ground-hopping. The big cat was weighing chances, and keeping track of Gallacher's boot. One day Spider was off guard, and Gallacher out of sight, and Scotch Jimmy was in like a flash, with every fish-hook on his front paws ready to clutch and his big teeth set for some deep surgery.

He got his claws on Spider—on, but not in, him. And he would have had them in too if Nip hadn't happened to come out of the back door at that very moment. She saw the whole thing at once and took it in her stride. In short, she went for Scotch Jimmy.

She got in one bite, and took two sets of claws on her black nose; but she got the cat off the owl. In the process she sent Spider on his back, and the owl didn't like it. When she ran forward to sniff him after chasing the cat she got his claws fixed right where Scotch Jimmy had already drawn blood. And, of course, Nip didn't like it.

But—and this is the strange thing—instead of making a meal of Spider she scuttered for the house with her tail pressed into her seat, then peeped out of the back door with her ears pinned down. She, who bit at the biggest feet that trampled her, who bossed cats and dogs and slew rats by the sackful, ran in deadly fear from a little tawny owl with big claws who thought he was being attacked when his life was being saved.

From that day the owl went in fear of the cat, and Nip went in fear of the owl. But the owl's fear was great, while Nip's was little and Scotch Jimmy's fear of the terrier was greater than either.

Along about harvest time there was something of a *rapprochement* between Nip and the owl. By then Spider was full grown and well moustached, strong and silent in flight, and beginning to hoot. The bitch could move freely in the yard again at night, and he even allowed her to rummage about in the barn when he was roosting on the rafters. Every once in a while he would drop silently on her and clutch at her rump, but there was no savagery in the attacks and the terrier soon treated them as a normal working risk that was annoying rather than dangerous.

The first corn was cut when Spider started killing mice and voles. And, inevitably, his first catch was made at the expense of Scotch Jimmy.

S.J. was jungled up among the hemp nettles and hogweed at the bottom of the stackyard hedge, with his tail-tip twitching nervously and his ear hairs trembling in the wind. A fat vole, with boot-button eyes, was scurrying among the purple clover a little way out from the hedge, and Scotch Jimmy was waiting for it to scurry in his direction.

When it did eventually begin to come his way, hesitantly and with many aimless detours, S.J. thrust his moon face forward and began to shuffle his hindfeet ready for the spring. But ready was all he got. Just as the vole came within striking distance, a shadow passed between Scotch Jimmy and the sun, and Spider was down, and up, and away with the vole, leaving the dumbfounded cat glaring murder.

Scotch Jimmy sneaked away down the hedge, under cover, with his thick tail jerking in anger. Spider gulped his vole, blinked, and said "wee-wick" softly and throatily. Scotch Jimmy halted once, with lifted paw, to glower over his shoulder at the owl. The feud was on till death do us part.

Spider caught his second mouse in the barn while Gallacher was gathering sacks of grain. Gallacher saw the mouse scurrying, then he saw the owl, and before he knew it there was Spider on his shoulder, chirling musically in his ear, with the mouse clutched in a foot. Gallacher stroked him, and the owl, closing his big eyes, rubbed the side of his head against a cheek bristling with two days' stubble.

"Clever wee man," the big man growled, beaming. "Och, you're the gran wee bird, sure enough!" Spider crooned, Gallacher crooned and said nonsensical things, but caught himself on before he got the length of *diddums catchums wee moosie*, which was the way he was headed.

Instead, he said: "Noo that you're workin' for yoursel' I'll be leavin' ye to fend for yoursel'." Then he shouted for his wife. "Hey, wife, come and see: Spider's catched hissel' a moose!"

Each night three hunters went to work—the owl, the terrier and the cat; a mouse brigade hunting independently of each other and of all the other hunters on the farm. Then one morning Gallacher found Nip marking at the drystane dyke in the stackyard, and presently saw a weasel poking its triangular head from a hole. And the big man flared up in anger.

"Here, Nip!" he shouted in his best hayfield voice, at the same time slapping his thigh with a big, calloused hand. "Cummeer, you little bugger you . . . that's a Johnny Whittret . . . leave it, dug, damn you! That's no for killin'!"

Gallacher expected great things from his Nip.

During this one-sided conversation the weasel made his way to safety by devious dyke highways, and when Nip slipped quietly back to the spot the musty odour was no longer there. That was her first weasel, and she was disappointed at not being allowed to taste it.

The weasel, or whittret, was back in the dyke in the morning. She was a small, dapper little beast, in foxy-red coat and white waistcoat, so tiny, indeed, that many farmers would have called her a mouse-weasel, believing her to be of a different species, while she was merely of a species where the females are notably smaller than the males. All weasels were Johnny Whittrets to Gallacher, who took no account of their sex for the sufficient reason that he couldn't have told anyway.

Johnny Whittret, in the present context referred to as "she", was shifting ground, as weasels frequently do. But she was drawn by the mice in the Mossrigg stackyard, and by the rats in the out-buildings, so she was prepared to linger. Gallacher saw her for the second time two days after he had rated Nip for showing an interest in her.

It was the day after that again that Johnny Whittret completely won the heart of Gallacher of Mossrigg.

The big man was at the back door blethering to the postman when the byreman suddenly shouted: "There's a wheesel in the dyke there, Wull!"

And sure enough there was. The byreman ran for a stick to clout with, while the postman shouted: "Where's the dug?" Gallacher froze them both with a double-barrelled, apt and unprintable epithet, then called to his wife in the kitchen to come and see.

The weasel was moving up, and down, and along, the face of the dyke like an electric spark, defying the laws of gravity. Gallacher became impatient and called to his wife again: "Come awa wummin and see!" Byreman, postman, and farmer stood stock still watching the whittret.

Mrs Gallacher came at last, with dough on her hands and Nip at her heel. And Gallacher exploded in her face.

"Get that wee scunner inside. Are ye daft, wummin? She'll kill the whittret sure if she gets near it. Shut the door!"

Nip, wondering what it was all about, was shut inside, where she stood harking with her tail between her legs. Then round the corner, panthering, and full of his own importance, came Scotch Jimmy.

Gallacher swore. "A man canny get peace tae blaw his nose in this place. If that cat gets his eye on the whittret . . ." He hunkered down, genuinely anxious, and called to the cat in what he considered a fetching voice.

"Come tae me, puss; nice puss. Come on, Jimmy lad, that's the boy!" Scotch Jimmy came forward slowly, with tail upright, purring loudly.

"Nice puss!" Gallacher said to him. Scotch Jimmy rolled on his back and mewed. "Come on, boy," Gallacher wheedled, "nice pussy." Then, under his breath: "Come on tae me you big ugly bastard!"

Scotch Jimmy came on, and was caught and shut in the meal-house, and that was that. Postman and byreman knew better than to pass any comment. Said Gallacher: "Noo we can watch the whittret. . . ."

Johnny Whittret disappeared between a sandstone and a whinstone into the dyke. And for two minutes there was silence. Then from the heart of the dyke came the squealing as of a pig in distress.

"There y'are!" shouted Gallacher. "The whittret's gotten a rat! An' ye'd a' ha'e stood there an' let the cat or the dug kill it."

The squealing died, and presently the weasel came out backwards from the dyke, tugging the rat by the neck. She let the body fall to the ground, then whisked down after it, neat and needling as only a weasel can be.

Now, it was a big rat, all of a pound and a quarter in weight, while she was only a little weasel of three and a half ounces, but she took it by the neck, and pulled and pushed and wrestled it for fifteen feet along the ground to a heap of red tile drain-pipes. And into one of these she laboriously stuffed the body, after standing it almost upright by main strength.

"You never saw the like o' that noo on television, eh?" the big man laughed, as pleased as if he had arranged the whole thing himself.

"You can get back tae work noo," he said to the byreman. "An' see that that cat stays in the meal-house!" And when his wife said she must get back to her baking he was quick to warn her: "Noo see that the dug disna get oot, mind!"

The postman waited on. "Did ye ever see two rats, Wull, takin' awa an egg, wi' the wan rat lyin' on its back an' the ither draggin' it by the tail. They tell me . . ."

"Wheesh, man!" Gallacher interrupted him. "There's the whittret again!"

Johnny Whittret was sparking about the face of the dyke, clearly excited over a new smell. The men watched the hole into which she disappeared suddenly, and again to their ears came the surrender squeal of a rat. And again the weasel came out backwards, dragging a rat—not such a big one this time, but still more than three times her weight. It, too, was dragged to the heap of drainpipes, and hidden, and the weasel returned to the dyke.

"Great work," said the postman. "I never saw the like. But the dug'll kill it as soon as your back's turned, Wull. Hoo can ye expect tae keep her awa fae that dyke?"

"I'll speak tae her!" said Gallacher, and the postman wondered if his leg was being pulled.

It was; but Gallacher did speak to Nip. He took her to the dyke, and once she owned the weasel smell, he lectured her about it, holding her by the loose skin of her neck and driving home his point with the single word *No* repeated many times. Nip stayed away from the dyke all that day, but she was there on the following morning after Gallacher had gone to market.

When the stacks were up in the stackyard Nip found weasel smell in them almost every day, but all she could do was hanker, for there was no way in for her. At nightfall, Spider would fly to join her, and sit on a leet, watching for movement on the ground below. He waxed strong on the rats and mice that were battening on the corn.

One day a great mountain of machinery clanked and clattered into the yard—the threshing mill. Nip danced round it, barking excitedly; Scotch Jimmy shot twelve feet up a tree with his tail like a bottle brush; Spider flapped lazily from the stable rafters to see what it was all about. When the mill moved into position in the stackyard it was accompanied by the men, Nip, two collies, six cats, and Spider. Scotch Jimmy was still up his tree.

The mill started up with much noise, and was fed with sheaves by the men on the stack. Gallacher fastened the sacks to catch the clean, spilling grain and the air became filled with oat dust. Nip sat on a pile of straw, relaxed, waiting for the men to fork down to her level. She had been at a threshing before. Presently Spider flew down beside her. When she sniffed him he crooned. He was more than a little nervous in such a large company of cats.

The rats started to run when the men reached the last layer of the first stack. Nip took five in her stride, and five backs were broken by her flashing teeth. The collies had a rat apiece. Scotch Jimmy, arriving belatedly for the hunt, got clouted with a pitchfork by accident. Spider flashed down and up with a half-grown rat in his claws, and one of the cats, chasing a mouse on the mill, went through the mill and came out like a doormat.

"Hell's bells," said one of the men, "a man canny get a clout at a rat for dugs, cats an' hoolets. Man, Wull," he said to Gallacher, "when did ye start gaun in for hoolets?"

"Och, it's anither mooth tae feed," said Gallacher, "an' a man canny ha'e ower mony mooths tae feed when it comes tae rats. Wid ye no' like a bit guid rat yoursel'?"

Nip was sniffing at the next stack before the men started on it and when one of the collies came up to her, anxious to share the smell, she growled to warn him off. He growled back at her and they flew to the clinch.

"That's enough, Nip!" bawled Gallacher, but she was deaf to his order. So he rushed at her and grabbed her by the tail, and hoisted her. But she gurried on, and had the collie's fore-feet off the ground before her grip was loosened.

"Noo, you stay away fae her, you!" Gallacher ordered the collie. "That's my wee wife," he said to Nip. "But you jist stick tae rats the noo! Ye can bite Glen ony time ye like efter we're loused." And the men, watching, wondered.

Nip returned to her smell. Johnny Whittret was in the stack. The men didn't know it. Gallacher didn't know it. But Nip knew it. She wagged her tail when the men started on the stack, and was in among their feet, scraping into the sheaves, when they were still three feet from the bottom.

"Wait a wee, wummin," one of them shouted at her. "There's still a wheen o' coorses tae go."

Then Johnny Whittret broke out, like a red spark blown by the wind, streaking for the next stack as Nip and Scotch Jimmy moved. Almost in the same moment a great grandfather of a rat leaped down, to go scurrying in the same direction.

"A weasel!" shouted one man, swinging his pitchfork.

"A rat!" shouted a second, throwing his.

Nip, dodging the flying pitchfork, rushed for the rat. S.J. flashed after the weasel. Gallacher rushed at the man who had swiped at Johnny Whittret.

"Drap that, you eejit, you!" he bellowed. "Fork shafes an' never mind the wheesel. Whit the hell d'ye think it's daein'— eatin' corn?"

Nip got her rat, which squealed once, and bit her before its back was broken. She stood back from it when it was dead and allowed Scotch Jimmy, returning crestfallen from his futile chase of the weasel, to sniff it over disdainfully. Totally uncompromising about her exclusive ownership of live rats, she was prepared to share the dead ones with anybody.

"I'm surprised she didny go for the whittret, Wull," said the man who had thrown his fork at the rat.

"She's got mair sense than some folk," laughed Gallacher, winking. "Onyway, she kens better: I gi'ed her a talkin' tae this morning!"

The men returned to forking sheaves. When the last course was cleared there were nine dead rats in the bottom, all with blood on their necks, and two live ones which attempted to run. Nip snatched the live ones and rendered them dead, and Gallacher, pointing to the nine, got his opportunity to lecture.

"That was your Johnny Whittret," he said to the man who had brandished the pitchfork. "Man—if ye'd kilt that beast . . ." He said no more. But he had made his point, and they all remembered he had weasels in his bonnet.

In the evening, when the threshing mill was silent, Nip went sniffing and snoaking along the stackyard dyke seeking smells. She was looking for rats, not weasels, and the dyke was a favourite haunt of hers. She found no rats, but she did scent Johnny Whittret, and was immediately on her toes. Lecture or no lecture, Gallacher or no Gallacher, she was determined to meet J.W. teeth to teeth.

She poked where the musk scent was strongest and tried to extract her by inhalation; but Johnny Whittret was not to be extracted by inhalation or otherwise. She was busy in the dyke. She was looking for rats, and was on the trail of one when she heard the sniffing of the terrier. The dyke was long, with plenty of highways, and she was having difficulty in moving in on her rat. And now here was a dog to cause complications. She couldn't come out to take short-cuts.

But the big rat couldn't come out either. So there was Nip marking up and down outside the dyke, while Johnny Whittret hunted up and down inside, and the rat kept on the dodge. By and by, when the sun was reddening in the west, Spider wafted from the barn rafters and pitched on the dyke to see what was going on. He said *Wee-wick* in greeting, and was answered by a growl, for Nip was thinking he had come to poach.

She kept her eye on him as much as she could, but without letting the weasel get out of her nose. Nothing would have persuaded her nose away from the hole in the dyke. Spider, for his part, kept his ears on Nip and his eyes on Scotch Jimmy, who was lurking among the tall hogweed unknown to the dog. Scotch Jimmy knew there was a rat in the dyke and, cat-like, he was content to wait for it coming out. Nip now knew it, too, but she was more interested in the weasel. Spider had no idea at all what it was all about, but he was prepared to wait and see.

Then everything happened at once. . . .

Nip went over the dyke because the scent had moved to the other side. At the same time the rat broke out on the side she had just left, followed by a russet streak who was Johnny Whittret. Scotch Jimmy moved when the rat broke, and Nip flashed back over because she knew she had been fooled. Spider, seeing the rat, launched away with a wild war whoop and talons clutching. The weasel, shocked at the arrival of a menagerie round her ears, vanished into a mousehole like a streak of lightning.

What Nip saw was Scotch Jimmy. She saw the rat, of course; but she also saw that Scotch Jimmy was after it—after her rat! That decided her. She ignored the Johnny Whittret bolting for the mousehole. She ignored Spider swooping above her head. She rushed at Scotch Jimmy, bowled him over, and removed a piece of his ear. The cat tried to rake her face, but she dodged him and reached for his neck. That was warning enough for the son of Satan. He knew he might have her eyes; but he knew she would have his life. So he fled. And Nip turned for the rat.

But the rat was gone! She almost stood on her head when she outran its scent-line. Nip looked up, bewildered, for assuredly that was the way the rat must have gone. . . .

It was, indeed, on the byre roof—dead, in Spider's feet. Spider, watching the antics of Nip, circling to find a line that wasn't there, said *Wee-wick* and inflated his throat. Nip said *Waugh-waugh* and darted to the mousehole that held the weasel. Her anger having overcome her worldly wisdom, she poked in her nose and sniffed. Johnny promptly bit her right on the wet, chill, black tip of it. And, of course, she started to dig.

She was still digging when Spider had eaten half the rat and gone to roost with the other half under his feet. She was still digging when Gallacher came home half an hour later. And she was back looking for smells in the morning. By then the Johnny Whittret was lying in a drainpipe, dead and stiff in the teeth of a gin set by a keeper who knew little about weasels, except how to kill them.

And all that was left of the rat was an owl's pellet and a tail lying on the barn floor.

The Three Mates of Kyack the Falcon

CRAIG n'Iolair had for long been the crag of the eagles. Two empty grass-grown eyries, fronted with woodrush, high above the corrie, bore witness to the royal occupancy. But now the eagles were gone—shot and trapped by a man who dreamed the age-old pipe-dream that grouse would increase ten-fold when the great marauders were slain.

Two summers came and went, summers when the grouse numbers dwindled, and when the second season of long nights and freezing dawns came round there were few birds calling in the heather. Disease ravaged the hill, and disease can kill the red grouse faster than any eagle. Then came jackdaws—eight pairs of them—to goister about the eagles' rock, and preen in the empty eyries, and nest in rabbit burrows on the brow of the crag. The jackdaws joined the grey crows in quartering the moors by day, seeking grouse eggs which they spiked, and held aloft in their beaks, and drained. In one day the shells of ninety grouse eggs were scattered on the heather.

At hatching time the red grouse tried to hide their cheepers on the sheep walks, under over-arching heather; but the sharp-eyed crows and jackdaws found them, and many downy chicks died within sight of Craig n'Iolair. Nothing raided the nests of crow or jackdaw, so their eggs hatched, and their chicks fledged and flew, and lived because there was no eagle to fall upon them from the sky with a mighty rush of wings.

The man who had slain the last of the eagles now turned upon the crows. He set gins for them in peat hags, baited with eggs containing strychnine. But crows, whether they are grey-bodied hoodies or silver-eyed jackdaws, are not eagles: they are cunning, shy, wary, alert, resourceful, intelligent—unlike the lordly eagle, who is slow-witted, unsuspicious, unwary of traps. So the keeper's eggs weathered, and cracked, and oozed, and rotted in his gins, and few hoodies or jackdaws died the death of clenched feet.

Then one day, when the peat hags were filmed with ice and the master stags were roaring in the glen, a strange bird pitched on the eagles' rock; a blue bird with long wings and white breast barred with black: a fierce, proud-eyed, arrogant bird, with a hooked beak, mighty talons and flat, rakish head: a royal bird with the wind in his wings and death in the clutch of his foot—Kyack the peregrine, beautiful among the lordly ones, bold and brilliant flier, the king of all the falcons.

Kyack huddled, hunch-shouldered, on his perch, standing on one spread-taloned foot, with the black claws of the other upheld, showing through the barred feathers of his breast. His brilliant, far-seeing, hazel eyes, hard and unwinking, glared fiercely at the wild landscape falling away far below him. He liked what he saw. This was for him—this stern wilderness of high, heather flats and higher peaks; of deep glens and brooding pine forests; of razor-back ridges and wild waters and steep, stupendous screes.

He had come a long way in his quest—from the towering, sea-tormented cliffs of the west, where once the great sea eagles cast their shadows on rainbow waters—a young male seeking a range of his own, and a mate, and both for life. He had found the first: he would intercept the second. Or, if no gangrel

falcon appeared, he would fly out when the mountain black-
birds flew in.

Above him the jackdaws dipped and wheeled and threw
about the sky, *clacking* their protests; more than thirty small
black crows, with grey napes and glittering eyes, united against
the invader of their territory. They were noisy; they were
angry; but they were also afraid. They had never seen his like
before; yet they knew he was no harmless mousing kestrel,
or heather-skimming sparrowhawk. Instinctively, they knew
there was lightning in those folded wings, and death in the
spread-taloned foot. So they kept high, and mounted
higher, in widening circles, voicing their plaint from a safe
distance.

Far below, the grey crows were flapping, circling, pitching,
on the lookout for death or carrion, as yet unaware of the
intruder. Down among the peat hags Kyack saw big stags
herding hinds, and others, with swollen necks outstretched,
bellowing their challenges, for these were the days of
roaring.

Above the crows a raven soared, *prukking* hoarsely, a dark
shape against the sky's luminous blue. Higher still, almost
level with the eagles' crag, a great brown bird was drifting
on wide wings—the only buzzard on the range, whose mate
had fallen to the gun of the man who had slain the mighty
eagles.

For some moments Kyack watched the wheeling buzzard;
then he blinked and turned his head when one of the crows
left its fellows and came flapping up towards the crag. The
black-and-grey bird turned sharply away when he saw the
falcon, *kraa-ing* his discovery to everything within earshot.
Three times he circled the corrie, snarling his taunts to the
falcon; then, growing bolder, he swept down over Kyack's
perch, as if trying to hustle him from the crag.

The membrane flickered over the falcon's eye, and he
lowered his upheld foot. He said *kek-kek*, softly, to himself,
and scissored his wings. Then with a flick of his long pinions,
he hooked from the rock, turned side on, flicked his wings
again, and tilted forward. The crow knew then what was
coming, knew that he had made the great mistake of his life.

With a terrified squawk he dived earthwards, faster than he had ever moved before.

Fast? Yes, he was fast. And he went down like a falling leaf to put the falcon off his stroke. He flapped and banked and turned; he cut every caper he had ever learned, and many he had never cut before. He heard the ominous rush of wings, the hiss of air in the stiff webs of feathers—heard, and tried to elude them. As well try to elude the light of the rising sun or fly over the rainbow.

Down—down—down—came Kyack; a tight wedge, a feathered missile, a rushing thunderbolt of feathers, and— thud! The impact could be heard half a mile away. The crow faltered, turned, collapsed, and fell earthwards—a shapeless, twisting wreckage of feathers, struck dead from the grand stoop at 2,000 feet on a clear frosty morning with the red stags roaring.

Kyack pulled out of his dive when the crow's neck snapped, and threw up with effortless sweep of wings. He was on his perch again, with the foot drawn up into his breast feathers, when the body of the crow crashed among the lichened rocks more than 2,000 feet below.

Thus a new lord came to the crag of the eagles, and from that day the wise crows avoided the corrie. When their business took them that way they swung wide as they approached lest they call down the wrath of the watcher on the rock. The jackdaws fled from Craig n'Iolair and sought refuge in lesser crags far down the glen.

But they were still on the new lord's hunting ground, and during the short winter days many met death in the sky, to fall ragged and broken on the snow, with heads almost severed from bodies and blood threading scarlet from ebony beaks. Only the ravens remained on the crag, for the black birds of Odin feared neither eagle nor peregrine.

The keeper found many black feathers beside blood spatters on the snow, and wondered. Then he saw Kyack pitching headlong into a pack of hurtling grouse, and wondered no more. Instead, he almost burst a blood vessel. More vermin! He could already see his grouse melting away. So he who had slain the lordly and the mighty, the rare and the beautiful,

and nailed them to his vermin board to feed the maggots of
the blowfly, hurried home for the weapons of war to destroy
the highwayman in blue.

From that day he was never without his twelve-bore shotgun,
in addition to the ·22 automatic he always carried slung over
his shoulder on the hill. But the snows shrank and melted,
and the time of leafing came, and still Kyack kept out of gunshot. Nor could he be surprised on the crag.

When the red stags were in early velvet, and the blackcock
holding dawn tournaments on the open hill, two falcons
roosted on Craig n'Iolair. The keeper saw them playing
together above the tops, twisting and turning, and stooping
at each other in mock assault with wild, glad cries. Kyack had
found a mate, a wandering falcon of greater bulk than himself,
and was seeking to attract her to his domain.

One morning he flew up and down the rock face, alighting
on one ledge after another, calling *wee-choo*, *wee-choo*, *wee-
choo*, coaxingly, to the falcon. He was inviting her to choose a
nesting place. She was attracted to the old nest of a raven, in
a niche where aspens grew, but stones were heaped in it and
she could not sit.

Most of the stones were too heavy for her to move with beak
or shuffling wings, but she kept turning on the nest, trying to
clear a space in which to sit. She scattered stained bones and
rotted flesh and sodden black feathers—the remains of young
ravens killed by the stones which the keeper had dropped in
the nest; but she could not breast down a space in which to
settle. So she left at last with Kyack, to prospect along other
ledges.

She found another raven's nest, built of sticks and heather,
and thickly lined with wool which the carrion birds had torn
from the carcases of braxies. The nest was on a rock spur,
fronted by drooping woodrush. Above it, the rock face rose
sheer, black and water-veined, fissured, and bearded with green
moss. On a ledge beside the nest, half buried among grass and
blaeberry, were the bones of deer and sheep—all that remained
of the carrion which the birds had carried there the previous
year.

The falcon settled in the nest and turned round and round

in it slowly, flicking her wings. She rose and walked flat-footed round the edge, trampling the heather flat. She chuckled *Kwo-tik*, and settled again, blinking her proud eyes. She had made her choice.

But Kyack, the tiercel, and Kwo-tik, the falcon, had been seen by hostile eyes. The keeper, seated in the heather, and using his walking stick as a rest, viewed them through his telescope which he had drawn to ×40 magnifications to have them right beside him. The birds loomed large in the object lens, and the keeper could see the glittering highlight in Kyack's eye and the pink tongue of Kwo-tik when she opened her hooked beak. He spied up and down the rock face, and every detail of the nest, then snapped the telescope shut. For two days he checked them over, just to be sure they were nesting, then he went into action.

Kwo-tik was ready to lay her first egg when she heard the frenzied screaming of her mate above the corrie. She stood up in the nest and peered over the edge. On the slope below she saw a man in check tweeds and hob-nailed boots, breasting the steep with the aid of a stick; he had a gin trap slung over his shoulder and a black-and-white dog at heel. The falcon stood with legs braced widely apart, and head up, mute, till he was only a hundred feet below the nest. Then she lowered her head and called.

Kek-kek-kek-kek-kek!

Thus she greeted him; then with a mighty thrust of wings she launched from the nest, turned sharply in a vertical bank, and shot up to join Kyack in harrying the intruders with abuse.

The man came on slowly, with the easy step of one used to long hours on the hill, ignoring the angry demonstrations of the falcons. His boots struck sparks from the rocks. He had to claw his way up the last fifty feet of the crag, using hands and stick together, and the gin, swinging out from his shoulder, *clunked* against the rocks.

Above him the falcons dived and screamed. They came down at him like fighter planes; they hurtled along the face of the crag, swerving and banking; they stooped at his head, sheering away just when it seemed they must strike. All the time they screamed at him—while he visited the empty nest, while he clambered back down over the rocks, and until he left with his dog. Not once did the keeper cast an upward glance, but there was a pleased smile on his face as he walked out of the orbit of their abuse.

Presently, Kwo-tik wheeled down and pitched on the edge of the nest, with Kyack on her tail. While the tiercel perched on a twisted aspen above the nest, Kwo-tik walked flat-footed to the centre, ruffling her breast feathers, ready to settle. Suddenly there was a metallic *click!*, and something leaped at her from the nest.

Kwo-tik screamed a terrible scream, and Kyack flashed from his perch. *Kek-kek-kek-kek-kek!* he called in alarm and fear as he keeled in tight figures of eight above her head. He saw her lifting and lifting, but always she was pulled back by the strange thing on the nest. When he saw she could not rise Kyack dropped down, hovered for a moment above the edge of the nest, then pitched nervously beside her. The falcon was held by one splendid foot in the steel teeth of a rusty gin.

She strained back against the pull of the trap, sitting on her tail, striking with her free talons at the thing which held her, and Kyack had to side-step to escape the buffetings of her mighty wings. She panted audibly, with sickle beak open and tongue raised and protruding. But there was no escaping the incomprehensible foe.

All day she struggled and twisted, breaking her tail feathers, bruising her wings, and chipping her hooked beak, till at last she was hanging by a foot from the edge of the nest, dishevelled and broken—a once proud and beautiful thing with the glaze of death in her eyes; and when she was dead there lay on the nest the plucked bodies of a red grouse and an oyster catcher, brought as offerings by her mate.

Towards evening, the man came back to the crag, and Kyack circled above him, screaming his defiance. When he reached the nest, the man removed the body of the falcon from the gin, which he reset. Then he looked up at the frenzied tiercel.

"Kick up as much noise as you like," he shouted at him, "but just come a wee closer and I'll blaw you to hell wi' this!" And he thumbed the safety-catch from his gun.

The keeper left with the dead Kwo-tik hanging from his belt

by the feet. Near his house was his vermin board—a long wooden erection like a bill hoarding—on which hung all his trophies, and there he nailed the body of Kwo-tik, beside the stretched, stripping skeletons of stoats and weasels; the shrunken, moulting carcases of Highland wildcats; the grinning masks of fox and marten; the stained, depluming corpses of sparrowhawk and merlin; and the eyeless corpses of crow and jay, jackdaw and raven.

But the dead Kwo-tik did not hang for long with a nail through her neck. The body was taken down at noon the following day, and quietly buried in the midden, for the keeper had been warned by a neighbour that the law protected falcons, and that if the wrong eyes saw the dead peregrine the police would soon be heading towards Craig n'Iolair.

Not until his mate had been twenty-four hours dead did Kyack fly out to hunt. He made his first scouting sweep at 2,500 feet, with the sun on his back, touching the blue and ermine of his wings. He went round the shoulder of the mountain at high speed, thrusting every inch of the way with his long pinions, cleaving the air like a missile, tight-feathered in the flow of the wind. Far below, the sun stabbed the blue waters of the lock with flashing dirks, plunging them deep into the crested wavelets crawling slowly towards the shore where black cattle grazed under haloes of flies.

The east side of the mountain was steep, treacherous scree, which reached right down to the river and a reed-fringed lochan in the glen. A thousand feet above the river, and following its course, a mallard drake was flying, like a fat-bellied bottle on wings. He was flying fast, and already tilting in flight towards the blue waters of the lochan where sober-hued ducks were swimming with flotillas of downy ducklings.

Kyack side-slipped a thousand feet down the scree when he saw the drake; and heather, rocks, birch and aspen were blurred in the speed of his descent. Above a deep gully of raging waters he checked, and threw up and round in a dizzy corkscrew that sent the earth spinning below him. It seemed that he must crash at any moment; instead, he levelled off suddenly, and with a whicker of wings shot out across the glen, straight and true to his pitch above the drake.

The mallard saw him, as he had seen him from the moment he levelled off after his lightning, corkscrew turn on the mountain. He knew, without telling, that this was the crisis of his life. Fear spurred him to all-out effort, and his wings whistled as they beat the air. He tilted further the angle of his flight, and earth and water flashed below him. Then he sensed the falcon descending and opened his beak in a despairing *querk*.

Six hundred feet—five hundred—four hundred; the blue water of the lochan was rushing to meet the drake. His wildly beating wings were a blur, sending him in whistling flight through the air at sixty miles an hour. And then the falcon came down—all royal blue and white, with wings half closed; a feathered wedge hurtling from the sky with the speed of a shooting star.

The drake felt the sickening shock of the impact; his head went up as his spine cracked, and his body sagged and crumpled. Down, down, went Kyack with the impetus of his stoop; then his wings opened and he was rising vertically to meet the falling drake. As the spinning body passed him he turned tightly, flicked his wings, and dived to follow it. Bloody feathers eddied and drifted as the drake went down. When the body at last hit the rocks Kyack pitched and folded his wings beside it. After glaring about him he clutched the drake in a foot, and tugged it into an open space; then, with both feet on the body, he began to tear off great gobs of flesh from the breast with his beak.

For two days, no falcon was to be seen about Corrie n'Iolair, and the keeper spied for Kyack in vain. But he had not deserted his chosen range. On the third morning he was back, and a wonderful thing had happened.

The keeper saw him when the morning sky was red and the creeping mists rose-tinted with the sun. He was flying above the corrie, swooping playfully on another falcon—a second Kwo-tik with heavily barred breast and the mountains in her blood. The keeper watched them off and on during the day, circling and diving high above the corrie, and their glad screaming was a challenge and an affront to his ears.

The new Kwo-tik became Kyack's mate, and once again he

flew ahead of the falcon to every ledge and empty nest on the crag. He had no fear of the old raven's nest, because he had no inkling of what had happened there, such things being beyond his power to understand. So when the falcon showed a great interest in the fatal nest he made no attempt to dissuade her. Nor is it likely he could have done so.

Twice she touched down on the edge of the nest, and folded her wings; and twice she sheered off as if not quite satisfied. For a time she perched on a ledge near the nest, with one wing down, preening the feathers of her tail. Kyack lifted away and flew out to hunt. He knew she had made her choice.

When he came back half an hour later, with the rough plucked body of a cushat in his feet, she was on the nest again, crouching, with breast feathers ruffled. Kyack called to her, and she rose with her answering scream. Eluding her, he swooped down, and dropped the prey in the nest. It fell heavily, and obliquely, right on to the gin, and the teeth set to grasp the foot of a falcon closed on the corpse of a wild dove slain by her mate.

Thus it happened that Kwo-tik was able to lay her first orange-tawny egg in the nest without danger, and to cuddle it under her breast beside a rusty gin meant to take her by the feet at her first visit.

But the same hostile eyes were watching, and noted that two falcons were still flying about Corrie n'Iolair. So the man came again, and reset the gin; and Kwo-tik, having no knowledge of traps, flew back to her nest and ignominious death. Within three hours of the man's departure she was hanging by the feet—a dead Kwo-tik with the lids closing over her proud, proud eyes.

The keeper did not leave the gin on the nest, because he was certain the tiercel would not return there. He took trap and egg and the freshly killed body of a red grouse, as well as the body of Kwo-tik, and was happy about the day's work. He had a buyer for the dead falcon and her egg, and the grouse would taste all the better for being out of season yet within the law. The keeper was a man who thought of everything.

But Kyack did go to the nest, with a pipit in his claws, and if the gin had been left he, too, would have died. He hopped and skipped about the nest, with the pipit clutched in a foot, calling *kwo-tik: kwo-tik: kwo-tik* in low coaxing tones to the mate who was no longer there. Clearly, he did not understand what had happened to her. He knew only that she had disappeared. But he came many times to the nest that day before he realised she had disappeared for good.

So once again he was alone—attached to a nest containing only the carcase of a pipit, and the remains of a red grouse and a cushat. And once again he disappeared, this time for three days. When he returned on the fourth morning the wonderful thing had happened once more, and the keeper saw him flying above the crag with a third Kwo-tik cleaving the air by his side.

But the third Kwo-tik did not choose the old nest, with its rotting prey and record of infamy. She sought shrewdly over every crevice on the crag, and picked at last a shallow pocket in the rock, with a mere coating of peat and heather dust. There, without adding any kind of lining, she laid her first egg. And there, too, she laid her second before she was troubled by the man who had already destroyed two of her proud race.

He found the well-hidden nest without difficulty, for no man who seeks falcons, and knows them, can fail to find their eggs when he puts his mind to it. But he also found that it was much more difficult to reach than the other. From above, it was protected by twelve feet of sheer rock; below it the face was almost vertical for twice that distance. And, in addition, the eggs were hidden from above, so that stones could not be dropped on them to smash them.

So Kwo-tik laid her third egg, and presently was sitting close, fed by Kyack who brought her pipits and oyster catcher and pigeon and plover in the first four days. Then the enemy came again. . . .

Kwo-tik heard the screams of the watchful Kyack before she herself saw the man approaching the bottom of the crag. After spying him she sat close to see where he was headed. When he was in the corrie, she disengaged herself from her three warm eggs, and flashed from the nest to join her screaming mate.

The man toiled up to the rock above the nest. Tied to his belt was the same rusty gin which he would plant in the nest when he reached it, and it seemed as if another Kwo-tik would be hanging by the feet before the sun had set.

But the best laid schemes of keepers, like those of mice and other men, gang aft agley. And fate can overtake men as well as falcons.

The keeper had almost reached the top of the rock—indeed his fingers had grasped it, and he was on the point of drawing himself up—when the rope snarled in the heather and tugged at him. The tugging was enough to unsteady him and, after a moment of wild scrambling, he slipped and fell.

The rock tore the skin from his palms; it burred his knees. The scrub scratched his face, and cut his eye. With a great effort, he managed to grasp a rock-rooted aspen, and hang on till he found a footing. Having found it, he steadied himself, and jumped for the safety of a narrow ledge six feet below. He reached it, stumbled, and fell another twelve feet down the steep, scrubby slope. The scrub delayed his descent but did not stop him from breaking his arm against the boulder which finally brought him to a stop.

He was collecting his wits, flinching with the stouning anguish in his arm, when he heard the scrape of nailed boots on the rocks to his right. A tall man and a boy were hurrying towards him. The man coming to help him was the man who held him in complete contempt—Archibald Cameron of Corrie na Feidh, tenant of the hill farm, wearing green tweeds, a shirt of Locheil tartan, and a look of concern on his face. The boy with him was his son.

"Are you sair hurted, man?" he asked the keeper.

"My arm—I—think it's broken . . ." the keeper grunted.

"Let me see," said Cameron, and he looked at the arm. "Och, yes, I think you're right whatever," he went on. "I should say 'Hell mend you' but I won't. But I'm not saying you didn't ask for it!"

Every word went home like a dirk but the keeper ignored them. Instead he asked: "How did you happen—to be—here—the noo?"

Cameron, already fashioning a sling with necktie and handkerchiefs, frowned and said without heat:

"We were watching you, Alec and I, to see what were you

up to. You're one hell of a man, Donald! I know you killed a peregrine the other day and I made sure you were not going to be doing the same thing again if I could help it. I may only be the tenant here but you'll trap your next falcon over my dead body!"

The keeper started to say something, but Cameron cut him short.

"The next time I catch you at that nest, Donald, I'll have your liver for dog meat! But you won't be trying I'm thinking. The polis is waiting at the house for you. They've already got the bird and the egg, and the man you sold them to. . . .

"So let's see if we can fix this arm of yours and get you home to your missus. It must be hurting you sairly."

So the third mate of Kyack lived to rear her brood. She was visited only once before they flew—by Archibald Cameron's son; and he did not come with a gin to break her, he came with little aluminium rings and placed them gently on the legs of her chicks. Thus the eyases of Kwo-tik and Kyack were numbered, and their numbers noted in the British Museum, before they left Corrie n'Iolair to seek their separate destinies.

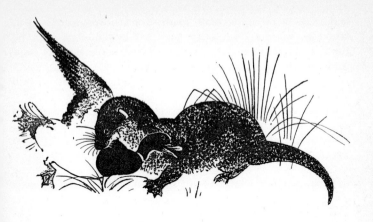

The Hunger Moon

FOR a week the daytime sky had been clear freezing blue; at night it was black velvet, studded with points of ice. Then came the change. The wind rose at sunrise, and by night-fall a cold gleaming moon was racing across a sky like a field of wind-blown snow.

One hour after midnight the snow came: not great, soft, feathery flakes drifting silently to earth, but sharp crystalline stuff that bit like points of steel, driven horizontally before a screeching wind. All next day the blizzard raged, piling up huge drifts on the high moor road and driving every moorland creature, hunter and hunted alike, under cover till its force was spent.

The wind died with the next daybreak, and the sun shone wanly from a cloudless sky. The cottagers hacked paths from their doorways through three feet of near-frozen snow. When the grey geese came arrowing down the sky in clamorous chevrons the ice on the loch was thick enough to carry a bullock; and there was hunger on the moor—hunger of the kind that stabs the belly as with a knife.

In the failing light of afternoon a big car lurched and bumped and skidded to the edge of the loch and stopped. Two men with guns came out and walked to a rough shelter of peat and hessian along the shore, near the high bank where the wild duck gathered at darkening. The men were wearing thick sea-boot stockings, fur-lined trousers, jackets and helmets (all Royal Air Force surplus) to insulate them against the cold.

Inside the hide they had folding stools, which they opened and planted firmly on the ground. They sat down, facing the frozen loch, and lit cigarettes. The cold was settling and their breath was vapour.

Down past the stackyard of Firknowe Farm, when the moon was bathing the wide levels of snow with blue-white radiance, came a lone dog otter. Travelling overland to the river he had been caught in the storm, and was holing up near the loch till travelling became easier. He knew the ground well, because he passed that way about three times a year. And he knew there were grey geese and ducks of many kinds to be found on the frozen loch.

His nose tasted the warm reek of hens in the Firknowe hen-houses, but he passed on without stepping aside. Not yet! One more hungry night and he might. . . . But not yet! His lack-lustre eyes glimmed fierce as he slipped past the stackyard, rudder pencilling the snow and fur gleaming oilily in the moonshine.

Through the trees fringing the loch, and he halted. Sitting upright, with forepaws on chest, he tested the faint wind fanning his face. His whiskers twitched. Ducks there were, and geese. Nothing else? No. He couldn't smell the men in the shelter because they were out of his line of scent.

The otter rippled on—a giant and beautiful weasel, black against the snow, running flank to flank with his own gliding shadow. Twice he stopped to listen, in upright weasel pose; but all that came to his ears was the faint, far hooting of a tawny owl, and the crickle of frozen snow under the webs of his feet.

The high peat bank was frozen and snow-crusted. The otter hesitated for a moment, then slid down on his belly to the ice below. There he sat up, with fore-webs palmed and whiskers twitching, to plot distance and layout.

The bank shadow cast by the moon hid the birds; it also hid the otter. Not a grey goose on the ice had sensed his coming. The ducks dozed on, all on one foot—golden-eye and mallard, teal, tufted and shoveller, and the moon smiled mirthlessly down.

Out on the moor a grouse chuckled throatily, questioningly, and three others, sheltering in crude burrows in the snow, raised heads to listen.

Eyes blinked and ears strained, and presently the heads went down again. The grouse were not hungry; they had fed where sheep had trodden the snow from the heather. But they were nervous. Once more the first bird chuckled, and again they were all long-necking to see what was afoot. Now they were uneasy, tensed to fly.

That whispering rustle as of a dragonfly's rubbed wings was not imagination, and they were not fooled. Croupy and cold they may have been, but not stupid. They knew it was the scrape of pads on frozen snow.

One beak opened and called *hurry-hurry*, and four grouse exploded into the air with whirr and tinkle of wings as a fox rushed the caller. The caller lost four tail feathers, but escaped with his life. The fox stood with brush down and head askew, slit-eyed and snarling, till their cries died away; then he drooled over their droppings and padded away with lurching gait towards Firknowe Farm.

The fox was The Limper—sly, seven and with one short leg. He had been wounded by gunshot as a sapling. Big William, the road-man, who had shot him, called him "the fox wi' the long short and the leg wan". This figure of speech was known as a Big Williamism.

Skirting the drifts on the wood-edge, The Limper trotted to the Firknowe stackyard and found the trail of the otter. Following it, he was pulled up short by a smell he didn't like—the smell of Man! Being wise, he back-tracked, and circled, keeping in the shadow of the stacks till he found the otter's trail again.

The man under the tarpaulin by the woodpile sat with gun on knees, chilled and chittering, waiting for grey geese coming in to pull wheat from the stacks; geese that wouldn't come tonight because they had fed elsewhere. He knew nothing of the passing of the otter, or of the fox which was trailing him down to the loch. Until he saw the tracks in the snow in the morning.

Away on the south-east corner of the moor, where the snow lay deep along the woodside, four dark objects moved from the trees across the moonlit level. They were two foxes and their accompanying shadows; dog and vixen hunting in couple, bound for the loch in search of ducks.

Ducks! There was the answer to all their problems. But ducks had their disadvantages. You got only one chance at them, and they were off—for many hours; perhaps for the rest of the night. But the foxes were ready to try.

That pair had already been to nine farms and two cottages, drooling over hen smell and hankering for blood. But every henhouse was barred against them, and there were no outliers to be chopped in barn or cart-shed. So now it was ducks or another day of fasting.

They trotted flank to flank, with heads down and tongues a-loll. Near the road the dog fox surprised and killed a weasel as it was nosing bird footprints in the snow. But he didn't eat it. Instead, he hid it under a peat overhang as a standby. If the pinch was sore he would eat it later, tough and rubbery and musky though it was.

Across the road they padded, out on to the open north shore of the loch, with noses to the wind-flaff and paws making scarcely a whisper on the frozen snow. A shadow passed between them, cast by a hunting owl which flew overhead without even a *whoof* from downy wings.

The cold was intense, penetrating, and the moon looked down sardonically. Ice crystals hung from the foxes' belly and brush fur, and tinkled like fairy bells. The vapour of their breath drifted past their flanks, which were lean and rib-taut with hunger.

In the peat-and-sacking shelter on the far shore the two men sat with guns between knees, chilled and stiff with waiting. The loch seldom froze; when it did there was hunger on the moor, and anything can happen when the Hunger Moon is high.

So they had come to see, being built that way. And they had come armed because they wanted a duck at the dawning, if they didn't find work for the guns before then.

They expected—or rather they hoped—that there would be callers in the night, calling on the massed ducks in the bank shadow, to drink their hot blood and so warm their own. For the hunters of the wild learn quickly, and the loch which was the ducks' refuge from peril had now been transformed by Nature into a right-of-way for their enemies.

Tonight, all roads led to the loch just as, at other times, all roads led to the potato fields, the turnip fields, the hay, the corn, the hedges or the rabbit warrens. Tonight, rabbits were in burrows, hares in the dangerous proximity of stackyards, and grouse on the lower ground—except for the few braving it out in burrows in the snow, and the few would soon perish, or leave.

The Limper was crouching in the shadow of a hummock above the loch, unseen by the men, watching the otter belly-crawling slowly towards the birds on the ice. He was wondering hard, because he had seen the car on the shore, and he knew that cars meant men somewhere.

He was nobody's fool, The Limper. He didn't know exactly where the men might be, but he knew they were there. And he wasn't forgetting it! That car. . . . Men wouldn't be out on a night like this just for the love of it.

Looking over his right shoulder as he crouched he saw two foxes moving up behind him. He was upwind of them, but out of their line, so he knew they wouldn't scent him if they kept their direction. He guessed they were out on the same errand as the otter.

The otter bellied on, leaving a shallow furrow in the snow. The two foxes came on behind. The men in the hide were still seeing nothing of the building drama.

Still The Limper waited, content to watch. He had no urge to join the other foxes. In his hardest winter he had never hunted in company. He watched the pair move skilfully to the shore and glide under the shadow of the bank. He watched them as they stalked out in the wake of the otter.

Three hungry hunters on the ice, and still the wary geese failed to sound the alarm. The Limper was amazed at them. But he was still preoccupied with the car. The car! That was the thing. There was something wrong with the whole set-up. But he couldn't figure it, and when The Limper couldn't figure anything he just sat still—figuring! That's why he was seven.

Suddenly the otter streaked across a neck of moonlight. His rush was swift, accurate, deadly. Wings hummed and webbed feet slapped the ice, and geese and ducks were in the air, in a milling rabble, clamorous and terrified, beating up into the face of the moon in a ragged circus.

On the ice a duck was flapping, with the otter astride him, and the otter tasted blood. But as the first trickle thrilled his palate he was interrupted.

Patter of pads on ice and the two foxes were closing in a converging attack on the otter. They snap-snapped with ivory fangs as the jaws of the duck killer opened to show still sharper teeth. The foxes snarled and the otter nickered, and the ivories flashed in the moonlight.

But what is one otter against two big foxes—two Scottish hill foxes at that, lean and hardbitten—with the plan all worked out and hearts full of fight?

Oh! he was dour enough, that otter, straddling his duck and ready to fight. They bit him. They chopped and cut him, and wiped his eyes with their brushes. He made them sneeze blood as they snapped at him. But if they were sneezing blood he was beginning to ooze it. So he quit, and slithered away across the ice in a rage.

And the reynards pounced on his duck—a fat mallard with a punctured heart.

The Limper, still crouched by the hummock, was beginning to wonder if he had missed his chance. He leaped down on to the ice and inched forward, but did not leave the concealing shadow of the high bank. He was tempted to go in and argue for his share. He was sure he could win the argument. But he was still worried about the car. Maybe he was being over-cautious, but he couldn't forget it was there.

Out on the ice, dog fox and vixen were proceeding to fall out over the duck. Both of them wanted it, and the dog fox was too hungry to let the vixen have all of it.

There's no saying what would have happened if the argument had been allowed to develop. It wasn't. . . .

Two shotguns roared as one, and the foxes were knocked kicking across the ice. The dog struggled on his back, like an overturned beetle, while the vixen tried to drag away with hindlegs shattered. Two men appeared suddenly, apparently out of the ice, and again the shotguns spoke; and this time the two foxes lay still, their argument unsettled.

"This must be visiting night, Geordie," said one.

"Aye! Twa foxes is good work. But this'll mean nae ducks at daylight."

"There's this one," said the other.

"Och, no!" said Geordie. "We'll leave it as a bait. We're in nae hurry. Some o' they stoat-weasels on the mair micht come lookin' for *their* Christmas dinner. We'll take thur foxes tae the car, and ha'e a hot drink, then we can watch the duck for a while yet."

So they picked up the foxes and walked back to the car. When they got there, with heavy burdens and empty guns, a third fox shot on to the ice, snatched up the duck in his stride, looked at them, and ran—thirty yards out of gunshot.

The men swore profanely, colourfully and originally, and The Limper grinned foxily. The car! That was the thing.

"Man!" said Big William, holding his dram up to the light in the village pub that afternoon, "you boys should ha'e been at the loch last night!"

The two men who had sat in the peat-and-sacking hide looked at each other, then didn't say what they were going to say.

"Why?" they asked instead.

"Man!" said William, "it was the funniest thing. There was an otter an' twa foxes had a fight aboot a duck—a mallard it was. The foxes got shote, but the otter got awa. An' I see there was a third fox, but . . ."

"Good Lord!" said one of the men. "Were you there, too?"

"Me?" said William. "Naw, man, I've mair sense than go stravaigin' aboot on a night like yon. Naw! I just read aboot it in the snaw this mornin'!"

After the Long Sleep

ONE morning the sun shone with a new warmth, and the cawing of the rooks became a more confident clamour. New odours, tangy and pungent, were distilled on the air as the dusty sunbeams probed through the withered raspberry canes crowding the bases of the rookery elms. On the south fringe of the rookery the ground was hillocky, and touzie with matted grass, bleached and rasping after the snell winds and savage frosts of the long winter. A solitary rook, disabled by small shot, was dibbling hopefully on one of the hillocks.

Vapour, like frost smoke, skeined from the hillocks as the sun's warmth breathed deep into the grass roots, where needle blades, already greener than the first leaves of beeches, were poking through the smother. Suddenly, the rook stopped dibbling, and stood with his head cocked to one side, so that he could bring the full glitter of his eye on the thing which had startled him.

A tussock on the face of the nearest hillock had moved; yet

there was no wind. The rook was curious to learn why. Becoming more and more amazed he watched the tussock shake, splay out, and actually come apart. The detached part suddenly rolled down the slope, straight for the astonished bird. With a startled caw he flapped back, buckling his broken wing, and sitting helplessly on his tail till he managed to jerk his flight feathers from under his feet.

"*Ach! Harr!*" he barked, rudely sticking out his wet, pink tongue. Then he stabbed the ground with his dirt-caked beak, and pretended to peck at something in the grass. The feathers on his head became suddenly erect; he was ready for battle. He had solved the problem of the rolling grass tussock.

A ghost of a sneeze came from it—the kind of sneeze you'd hear from a kitten at a range of twenty feet—and a sharp, pig-like snout poked out to view the world, and smell it. But the hedgehog, after his five months' sleep, had to do a lot more sneezing before he could smell properly.

He did a lot more, while the rook pecked at imaginary titbits, watching. Once or twice he tried to open wide his eyes, but the lids were still sticky, and he had to give up the attempt for the present. He couldn't see the rook, but he could hear him, and smell him; so, when the cocksure gentleman in the blue-black feathers stabbed at his partly sealed eyes, Mr Quills promptly tucked in his head, lowering his brow-quills forward and snuggling into his grass quilts again to think the matter over.

He must have been thinking (if he was capable of thought), "This is where I came in," for a leering magpie had plucked twenty-three barbs from his hide when he was rolling up his bedding before going to sleep at the beginning of the winter.

For the rest of the day the grass ball did not stir, and the rook, soon losing interest, hopped away on other business. At dusk Mr Quills uncoiled again. He chopped his teeth, shook off clinging grass and leaves, and contrived to scratch his left ear with his left hindfoot. His fleas were coming awake too! How he can manage to sleep so long, and so soundly—in a death-like coma—with so many fleas on him, is a mystery which no flea-sensitive naturalist has ever been able to solve. Mr Quills had an armoury of some sixteen thousand barbs (so they say) to protect him from his enemies; he was beginning to think he had just as many fleas.

By moonrise he had managed to shake off most of his blankets, and blink his eyelids unstuck. And he was very hungry. All the fat he had laid on his ribs in the autumn was long since used up and he was little more than a skeleton covered with hair and quills.

A tawny owl was whooping when Mr Quills ducked under the bottom wire of the rookery fence near the burn. He put his right forefoot between the Y stems of a dogrose growing on the bank, and was pulled up short. He tugged and tugged till he was almost exhausted, and it began to look as if he would have to uproot the dogrose and take it with him or part company with his foot. Actually, he did neither. He turned a somersault through the broad splay of the Y—whether accidentally or intentionally no one will ever know—and his foot slipped free as neatly as you like. He took time to admire it, and lick it, before he scrambled back right way up again.

With all the fuss and exertion he forgot what it was he had set out to do—eat. Trying to remember, he tucked in his nose, and went to sleep under the dogrose for two and a half days. When he opened his eyes in the dewy sunrise he chopped, scratched, rubbed ear against shoulder, and burst out of the briar patch as if he had just overslept by five minutes and had an urgent appointment somewhere.

Off across the big rookery pasture he shambled, leaving the plain trail of his going on the silvery dew which filmed the grass. Sheep, nudging lambs, stamped their feet at him; rabbits sat up with ears pointing skyward to watch him; the peewits whooped and looped above him on woollywings. Rooks, flying out from the elms, swooped low and cawed to their followers. A hedgehog in broad daylight! Mr Quills was affronted; the rooks dumbfounded; and the textbooks torn up for wastepaper. I could tell you what Mr Quills was thinking (supposing he could think) but no respectable printer would set the type. . . .

Mr Quills wanted to get to the Summerfield ditch—quickly. He found it by the supremely simple expedient of falling into it. Dripping amber-coloured slime, he waddled down the ditch till he found a way out. When he climbed out, breathing with mouth open, he left an orange trail on the silvery grass.

Near the ditch, under a big thorn with bark scuffed and torn by the horns of cattle, he found a sodden wooden board bearing the fading inscription MARGARINE, and flipped it over deftly. He knew he would find a multitude of woodlice underneath; and did. When he had licked them all in, he rolled himself into a burrow under the thorn and went to sleep for the rest of the day. He was still drowsy with the dregs of Hibernatum Bromide.

In the near-twilight of sunset he squeezed through a gap in the drystane dyke into the kitchen garden of Summerfield Farm, still far from wideawake but tremendously hungry. From underneath a gooseberry bush a white bird suddenly fled squawking, and Mr Quills' head went down at once. Then he had a brilliant notion—which proved right.

The little Light Sussex bantam, which had fled in such fright, had been laying away, and in her secret nest had laid one egg. Mr Quills sneaked under the pile of sere hedge clippings and found her egg: creamy-white, smooth of texture and warm. With a grunt of satisfaction he scooped out the egg with a forefoot and gathered it under his chin.

Mr Quills bit the egg; at least he tried to. But it slipped away from him, like a tablet of slippery soap through over-eager fingers. Mr Quills tried again; and again he lost it. Time after time he snatched at the elusive egg, till both egg and hedgehog were right at the bottom of the garden, under the boundary hedge. There the egg became lodged against the stem of a thorn. Mr Quills, drowsy again, flopped down on top of the egg and went to sleep—not realising he had at last broken the egg because it was wedged against the hawthorn.

He woke up with his face dipped in the yolk, and spluttered. Then he ate it, shell and all, and curled up again in the hedge-bottom. Before dawn he woke up and wandered away in the direction of the rookery, to find a hole under a tree root which he had used as a lair the previous summer. When he was less than twenty yards from it he slowed down to caterpillar pace, almost asleep. On the threshold of his lair, he stopped, swaying on his feet.

Suddenly, conscious of irritation, he twitched his nose. The irritation brought him out of his dwam. He wrinkled his nose again, and struggled against his stupor to find out what it was that was crawling over his face. It was a frog; and the frog was about as woolly-headed as Mr Quills. Mr Quills, collecting his wits more quickly than the other, snapped his jaws on one of the frog's legs and dragged it, struggling, into the hole under the tree. He slept with it held firmly in his jaws, and the frog slept too because there was nothing else it could do. Now and again it uttered a thin, reedy mew of protest.

Two more days saw Mr Quills almost back to normal waking fitness; his head was clear and his heart working at full pressure again. Once, before the hibernation torpor finally wore off, he allowed a big red juicy earthworm to cast two loops round his snout before he recognised what it was and gobbled it. That was the last time he was fooled.

But full faculties meant greater hunger, and, on the second day, just on daybreak, he hurried to a pond near the rookery. It was known to him of old, and he expected to find frogs spawning there. He found them, in hundreds—under the water, spreadeagled on the surface of the water, and in the shallows, with throats gulping. Mr Quills waded into the shallows, shouldering his way through masses of shuddering jelly. Right and left he snatched with his jaws; and right and left frogs dived to avoid him. These frogs were not at all woolly-headed.

But Mr Quills was not daunted. He waded on, and on, till he found himself out of his depth. He began to swim. He thrust his snout under the water, which gave the frogs something to think about. They began to crowd back to the shallows, with Mr Quills herding them, like a collie dog, and in the shallows he pounced and bit.

When he came ashore at last, shaking out loose water from his underfur, he had two frogs in his belly and a great, goggle-eyed, green and yellow female, bloated with spawn, in his jaws. Frog meat was good, especially for a hedgehog with the after-hibernation hunger, and Mr Quills liked it. Now he wanted a place where he could lie up for the day. The sky was brightening and the light strong. With the frog held firmly,

crippled but still alive, he shambled up the slope from the
pond to look for cover.

He was pattering up a long, flat slab of whin, leaving behind
him a trail of muddy prints, when he stopped short—con-
fronted by two blue-black stems. Mr Quills lowered his brow
quills, and inhaled deeply. The stems were legs, and the taint
in his nostrils was musk. Mr Quills arced up his snout, then
crouched on the slab. Leering down at him, with tongue
hanging from the side of his mouth, was a big red dog fox
with amber eyes and a head full of fox-nonsense.

Releasing his frog, Mr Quills coiled into a ball, knowing he
would roll down the slab; but, before he got started rolling,
the big fox pinned him down with a nimble paw. Mr Quills
squeaked. At the same moment there was the spiteful smack
of a ·22 Winchester, and fox and hedgehog rolled down the
slab together. The fox was kicking in death when he stopped
rolling. Mr Quills rolled farther, because he was a ball, and
fetched up two feet from the water's edge, terrified but quite
unhurt.

He crouched there without moving, not knowing the fox
was dead, and presently he heard footsteps coming down the
slab, which was red-splashed with the dog fox's blood.

Cameron of Summerfield Farm, with the Winchester slung,
cut the brush from the fox and threw the body in the pond,
sending the frogs swimming away with thrusts of hind-legs
from the splash. He had been waiting for the fox, and felt
rewarded for his loss of sleep. When he saw the hedgehog he
rolled the ball over with his boot and, noticing the beast was
wet, assumed the fox had been tipping it into the water. This
time he was wrong, but he might just as easily have been right,
for assuredly that was where the big fox was ettling to put Mr
Quills if he hadn't been interrupted.

Mr Quills remained coiled till long after Cameron had gone,
then he brought his face out under its armoury of barbs and
looked furtively about him. The man was gone; the fox was
gone; but the sun was up, turning the still water of the pond
on fire, and the frogs were croaking. Mr Quills pivoted on his
flat hind feet and raced for cover—any cover. On the blaes
slope, just above the water, he found a hole under a dogrose,

screened with grass and rootlets; it was not deep, and there were fragments of discoloured paper adhering to the roof. In the hole had been a wasps' nest, which had been torn out by a badger in the autumn.

For half an hour Mr Quills slept in the hole, with nose tucked against the palms of his hindfeet; then he was rudely awakened by something poking him where the doormat hair of his belly met the quill-line on his flanks. Instinctively, he coiled tightly, wideawake on the instant. He was poked again and again—obviously by an exploring paw—and rolled from his refuge into the full glare of the sun.

It is said that lightning never strikes twice in the same spot, which may or may not be true; certainly, under ordinary circumstances, Mr Quills would have been unlikely to run foul of two foxes on the same morning, within fifty yards and inside an hour and a half. But, as it happened, a vixen had chosen to den up close to the pond, which was in an old, worked-out whinstone quarry. Mr Quills didn't know this; nor did Cameron of Summerfield. Cameron had shot the dog fox; now the vixen, airting home, had found Mr Quills.

This, from Mr Quills' point of view, was more than usually unfortunate, for the vixen, being on her doorstep, so to speak, had all the time in the world. And the pond was right at hand. This was just the right kind of foolery for a vixen on a bright spring morning, especially when there was the prospect of a strong meal of hedgehog at the end of it.

The vixen, unlike her mate, was old; she knew north from south, and the time that men went to bed. She had much wisdom in her head and five cubs in her belly. Her teeth were worn and brown. She had two tusks missing, and only a tag of a brush, having broken teeth on one gin and lost half her tail in another; and she knew all there was to know about hedge-hogs.

What she didn't realise was that she was getting past it. When she pawed Mr Quills deftly on to his back, exposing the chink in his armour where his snout was tucked into his hind-feet, she discovered there was very little she could do about him, having no teeth worth speaking of. Of course, she pawed him about. She snarled at him, and bit at the air around him;

she submitted him to every indignity her fertile mind could dream of; but she could do nothing with him.

She sat down to ponder, with head cocked and brush curled round her hip. Mr Quills remained perfectly still, not seeing her but knowing she was still there. The vixen couldn't harm him so long as he remained coiled; if he tried to move she would have him. So it was stalemate; at least until the crow came down.

He was a carrion crow, with a flat head, ebony plumage shot with purple, and the glint of genius in his wicked eye. He putched beside Mr Quills, prodded the sod with his heavy beak, and said rude things to the fox; then he stabbed at the chink in Mr Quills' armour, which was still uppermost. Mr Quills lowered his visor and tightened his defences. The crow put one black foot on him, ready to strike again. And the vixen moved.

She rushed at the crow with stump teeth bared, thinking she would pin him down with a paw, then chop him. But the crow was airborne when she struck at the spot, and her jaws clicked on air, which made her feel a fool. She felt a bigger fool when the crow swooped behind her, and stabbed her viciously where her brush joined her rump. She chased him again, of course, missing as before. The crow taunted her with his harsh voice, goading her into running after him, and leaping at him, while he pitched, bounced, lifted and flapped above her head, always too quick for her paw-stroke and snapping jaws.

Mr Quills, perhaps realising this was the only opportunity he would be offered, shuffled back into the hole under the dogrose and wedged himself as securely as he could in the farthest corner. When the vixen returned she thrust her sharp face into the hole and sniffed; then she withdrew, bellied down, and tried to roll him out with a paw. But this time she could not move him; he was too firmly lodged.

She could have dug him out, of course; but, after scratching half-heartedly at the hole for a few moments, she decided against it, for what could she do with him anyway? Instead, with a great show of indifference, she trotted away to the far side of the pond, where she had her den in a hole under the rocks.

Mr Quills spent the entire day in his sanctuary under the dogrose, snuffling in sleep between long spells of wakefulness when he lay loosely coiled watching the entrance, wondering if the vixen would return. Then, at the first fading of the light, when the pond lay dark and the shadows were creeping up the face of the quarry in the last of the sunset, he poked out and shuffled away from the dangerous proximity.

Some hedgehogs have the unhappy knack of getting into one predicament after another, and the good fortune to escape from them, with or without outside help. Mr Quills was one such.

When he left the quarry pond he set off in the direction of Summerfield Farm, within half a mile of which he had spent his whole life; but he did not take the most direct route, or follow the field paths in the steps of Cameron. He spent three hours getting there, because he foraged the whole way—veering to left and right, zigzagging to the promptings of his nose, and running in half circles—snapping up a worm here and a slug there, and turning over leaves and loose stones for woodlice. By the time he reached the farm kitchen midden his feet were cold and the coarse hair of his belly was wet, but the edge was off his hunger. In the midden he found the skin of a kipper, which had a most attractive smell; he ate it and his hunger was sated.

Now, though the night was less than half spent, he wanted to lie up somewhere to digest his big meal, so he climbed out of the midden, which was merely a steep bank down which the farm refuse was tipped. The top of the bank was slippery, and Mr Quills lost his footing. The moment this happened, he did what he always did when he was about to fall: he coiled himself into a ball to let his quills act as shock absorbers.

The ball rolled down the slope, stotting among broken bottles, tin cans, egg shells, cabbage leaves, cardboard boxes and old tyres, and dislodged two quart tins which clattered down in its wake. Mr Quills came to a stop, on his back, with the lid of one tin underneath him, inside uppermost. It was the lid from a tin of scarlet paint and when Mr Quills, uncoiling, rolled off it, he was keeled scarlet on his back like one of Cameron's ewes. Then he trod on the lid, and the palms of his forefeet were scarlet too.

By the time he reached the stackyard he had walked most of the scarlet paint off his forefeet, but the bright daub on his back barbs remained. Among the corn stacks it was snugly dark, and still. On the thatch of one stack a white owl was sitting with a house-mouse under a foot; on the straw-padded ground below lay another which she had dropped earlier in the night. When hunting was good she often caught more mice than she needed, and sometimes she let them fall to the ground. Mr Quills snatched up the mouse, which was still limp, and bored into the stack-bottom with it. There he half-coiled and dozed with it held firmly in his jaws.

The white owl was still on the stack-top, standing with one foot drawn up into the feathers of her breast, when Mr Quills poked his head out again. Seeing him, she put both feet below her and craned forward to watch him with her dark, round, staring eyes. Mr Quills came right out, trailing lengths of straw, and ate his mouse on the spot. The watching owl, with her hypersensitive ears, could hear the cracking of bones as he chewed with the side of his mouth.

Daybreak was not far off. A chill wind was stirring. Gulls were crying as they flew overhead in the gloaming, and already the pheasants were *cu-cupping* in Summerfield Strip. The white owl lifted from the stack-top and flapped away, moth-like, on downy wings. Mr Quills, after licking his lips and sniffing the straw to make sure he wasn't leaving mouse morsels, shambled down the dark lane between the rows of corn-stacks, crossed the farm closs and, after crouching down for a moment when Cameron's Fleece barked suddenly, disappeared round the corner of the meal-house.

The meal-house was built hard against a dilapidated, fog-yirdit drystane dyke. Stack props of peeled birch poles, over-grown with bramble creepers, lay across the dyke with their tops resting on the meal-house roof. I don't know why Mr Quills should have wanted to climb on to the dyke, then from there to the roof by way of the props and creepers; but he did. Once he was up there, it was a near-certainty that he would fall off; and he did. Peering over the edge, he put too much weight forward, and toppled. He was coiling when he bounded off the guttering, and coiled when he landed with a splash—right in Cameron's rain-butt!

Fortunately for Mr Quills there was little depth of water in the butt, so he was not faced with the ordeal of swimming in circles till he became exhausted, then drowning. His plight was, nevertheless, serious. So long as he stood up he could keep his head clear of the water; but he had no hope of climbing out of the barrel. And the water was cold. Failing outside help, he would starve, freeze or drown. In the event, he was saved by Cameron's sheepdog Fleece.

Mr Quills was on his hindlegs, straining up, and padding round and round the barrel with his forefeet, when Fleece heard the scratch of his claws on the wood. With ears cocked and tail wagging, Fleece sniffed round the water-butt, but could smell nothing. The scratching, however, was real, so Fleece began scratching on the outside, barking as he did so.

His barking brought Cameron from the milk-house where he was scalding cans. Seeing Fleece at the barrel, and thinking there might be a rat in it, the farmer picked up a stout stick before coming to look. When he saw the hedgehog in the water he leaned his long body over the edge of the barrel and reached down with calloused hand to retrieve him. Mr Quills, alarmed, tried to coil. But that meant his head was under water, so he opened up at once, sneezing and spluttering, and allowed the farmer to slip a hand under his unprotected belly. Cameron gripped with strong fingers and hefted him from the barrel.

Mr Quills, still sneezing, and distressed after his ducking, made no attempt to roll up; he simply crouched in the farmer's huge palm, with his brow quills flat and his hind legs dangling. Cameron held him at eye level, studying him closely, till he noticed the flea on his wrist. He put Mr Quills down with alacrity then, squashed the flea with his thumb, wiped his hands on the seat of his trousers, and returned to the milk-house, calling on Fleece to come oot o' that.

It was ten minutes later before Mr Quills moved. After looking about him to make sure he was alone, he turned about and raced for the drystane dyke, where he soon found an entry between two mossed stones. And, inside the dyke, he half-coiled and went to sleep.

He slept fitfully through the noises of the day and when darkness fell with its near-silence, momentarily broken by the far barking of a dog or the stamp of a hoof on the cobbled stable floor, he tumbled from the dyke and shambled away to hunt.

The night was dark, cool, damp and still. Mr Quills followed the hayfield edge, where the young grass was smothering the old oat stubble. The endrigg was bitten close by rabbits. Nothing was moving; the field seemed empty of life. Then a dark shape, like a moving shadow, rushed across from the direction of the road, and suddenly peewits were throwing up, keening in alarm; scores of white fuds bobbed as rabbits bolted; and a roebuck, with fraying antlers, bounded in terror past Mr Quills, almost striking him with a hoof. He curled defensively as the panting dog rushed over him on the trail of the fleeing buck, and stayed coiled till long after it was gone.

On the burn-side flats, where the flowers of the butterbur, or bad man's rhubarb, grew in close rosettes under catkined alders, he hunted, snapping up worm and slug and centipede and woodlice as he moved. Like other animals defensively garbed, he was heedless of the noise he made. Snuffling along a bank where yellow celandine grew, he put a foot wrong, and rolled down, coming to a stop on a sandspit, on which was pressed the prints of many feet. The prints had been made by a brown rat when he was running to and from the half-eaten body of a hare which was lying on the edge of the spit. Mr Quills found the hare by its strong smell, and drew up to the body to feed.

It was while he was chewing on the hare that he heard the crackle of careless feet in the withered grass behind him. Mr Quills stopped eating to listen. The crackling continued, and he turned about to face the sound, and sniff. He liked what he could sniff, so he shambled towards the sound; he bored into the tussocks and liked what he found. There was a scuffling which shook the grasstops, and squeaks and grunts that could have been heard by an owl at a hundred yards range; then Mr Quills came out flank to flank with a big female hedgehog and led her to the feast.

They ran together for most of the night—and that is an

H

exact description, for Mr Quills chivvied and harassed his new-found mate up and down the burn, through the butter-bur, through the thickets, and through the old bracken stands on the slopes—and when the day-birds began to call, in the twilight of morning, they were both hot and thirsty. They shambled to the burn together, and drank noisily, side by side. But when they went to the sandspit for a last meal of hare, they found only fox-smell and a few fluffs of fur; the reynard had carried the body away.

The hedgehogs did not linger. They snuffed about the spit for a minute, then set out in the direction of Summerfield—with the female leading. Summerfield Farm was her world, too; her lair, indeed, was under the roots of a hedgerow sycamore not far from the farm stackyard, and that was where she was headed.

They were shambling along the inside of the hedge, now walking, now spurting on unseen legs, running a race against the spreading light in the eastern sky, when Mr Quills was pulled up short as if by an invisible rein. He grunted, and tugged, while the mate hurried on. She was curled up in her snuggery, fast asleep, while he was still fighting the rabbit snare into which he had walked.

He finished up with the noose biting into his quills, and the wire looped about a foreleg. When he tried to coil he could not. And that is how Pate Tamson found him at half-past eight in the morning, when he arrived with six rabbits hanging from his waist and ten snares in his hand.

Pate cursed him, of course, then pulled the peg and carried hedgehog and snare to Summerfield Farm, where he borrowed secateurs to cut the wire. Cameron, coming into the shed from the byre, looked at the hedgehog and said:

"That's the same wan I fished oot o' the watter-butt." He was grinning.

"Hoo d'ye ken?" Pate asked him, furious about his ruined snare.

"Because he's got ma keel mark!" replied Cameron. "A man needs tae ken his hedgehogs or somebody micht steal them. Turn him loose!"

Pate, who was ettling to knock Mr Quills on the head, put

him down instead and rolled him into a corner with his foot. He had the rabbiting of Summerfield Farm, gratis, and saw no point in crossing Cameron.

"The beast's botherin' naebody," Cameron said as they left the shed, "an' a snare's naethur here nor there. Onyway, that's likely the last we'll see o't. . . ."

But Cameron was wrong.

He was wrong, and knew it within a couple of hours, for when Mr Quills left the shed he crawled into a hole near the base of a corn-stack and, finding it warm and dark, burrowed into the straw. How was he to know that he had bedded down in a stack-nest used by the Summerfield hens?

He was conscious of the increased warmth when the first hen flew in, and he grumbled in his sleep while she was laying. Her cackling, as she left, startled him to wakefulness, and when he poked his head up through the straw he saw her egg. Wraxing out of his bed, Mr Quills sniffed at it. He tried to bite it but his teeth merely glanced off it, sending it rolling towards the entrance. He tried again, with the same result, and, because the egg was now lying in the full glare of the daylight, he turned back into the nest and coiled up to sleep again.

Presently, two hens flew to the nest together, jostling each other as they forced their way into the dim snugness. They turned round and round, tossed straws over their necks, then settled down side by side and beak to tail—right on top of Mr Quills. Mr Quills, finding the warmth of them insufferable, squeaked. The hens, hearing the squeaking, long-necked and blinked their eyes. Mr Quills heaved; the hens stood up alarmed. He heaved again, and they chuckled in query. Then he burst from the straw, right between them, and they flew squawking and shrieking from the nest.

Cameron and Pate were tinkering with a tractor in the stack-yard when the cackling hens gusted past them, and the farmer, guessing where they had come from and ever watchful for crows, rats and other raiders, hurried to the stack with Pate on his heels. He lifted the egg lying at the front of the nest then, reaching in with his hand, felt the barbs of Mr Quills.

"A bliddy hedgehog!" he exploded. He rolled Mr Quills forward and toppled him to the ground. Then he saw the scarlet keel marks. "Well I'll be damned!" he said, "if it's no' the same brit again!"

"Best chap it on the heid!" said Pate. "That's where your eggs have been disappearin'. Thur damn beasts can waste mair eggs than the Packin' Station!"

But Cameron was feeling at the back of the nest with his hand. "Nae wet bits there, Pate," he said. "An' nae broken shells. An' this egg's a' richt. The beast hisna touched ony that I can see."

"Take it frae me, he wisna in there for fun," Pate insisted.

"Mebbe he jist picked the first hole he could fin'," the farmer said, "him bein' frichted wi' the snare like. The fact is," he went on, "I dinna fancy the idea o' killin' hedgehogs. But if I get this chap in a nest again I'll sort him. . . ."

So Mr Quills, much to Pate's disgust, was rolled by Cameron's boot out of the stackyard and into the hayfield, and left to sort himself out from there.

And that made four times the farmer had saved Mr Quills' life since his awakening. The farmer spoke only of three times, but then he couldn't know that it was the same hedgehog he had saved from the fox.

Mr Quills slept that day in the hedgebottom, and met his mate at night. For some time afterwards he hunted with her nightly, not always beside her but never far away; and some days he shared her den under the sycamore. But, as the spring advanced, she began to show less and less interest in his company, and one morning he returned to the den to find that she wasn't there. Nor did she arrive later in the day. She had departed to find a new lair where she could give birth to her young, alone.

So Mr Quills became a bachelor again, hunting and denning on his own, waiting for the height of summer with its second season of wooing.

Gallacher's Wee Man

GALLACHER of Mossrigg was glad he had taken a notion to visit The Strip that morning, when the young corn was green in the drills and the cuckoos calling in the glen. And he spoke often about it afterwards.

"I don't know what took me," he would say; "I kent fine the bird was ticht doon on six eggs, but wasna even thinkin' aboot her. It was just a notion. But if I hadna went, I'm share he would ha'e whupped the lot!" And, having said this, he was wont to finish with a list of earthy epithets which questioned the new man's personal cleanliness, his state of mind, and the legitimacy of his birth.

He had stopped that morning at the end of The Strip, with hands thrust deep in go-to-hell pockets and the two collies at his feet. The Strip was a long narrow belt of mixed hardwoods and pines on the high-ground skyline, flanked by tall hedges of thorn. Kestrels, cushats, and black crows nested in it; partridges laid their eggs in the thick cover of the hedge-bottoms. In blustery weather the Mossrigg cattle sheltered in

it. Even during the war it had not known the ring of an axe.
Gallacher was a man of violent likes and dislikes, and he liked
The Strip.

He was in jovial mood as his grey eyes scanned his tidy acres,
and rested with pride on the white well-kept farmhouse four
fields away beyond the road. The corn was green; the tatties
were in; the hay was rushing up thick and lush and would be
ready for cutting early. The big man pulled a grass stalk,
which he bit, skelped a leg with his stick and called up the
dogs.

Suddenly, a harsh *kraa-ing* made him turn his eyes skywards,
and he smiled at what he saw: a little kestrel tiercel harrying
a big black carrion crow from the sacred boundary of his
nesting territory. Gallacher watched while the small falcon
drove off the crow, then was minded to take a look at the nest
while he was in The Strip. He knew it well enough, for one of
the things he did each May was to find out where the Mossrigg
kestrels were nesting.

And if you think that's a strange thing for a farmer to be
doing, you should know more about Gallacher of Mossrigg
and his neighbours. They knew the time of day. They were on
speaking terms with any fact that sat up and looked them
squarely in the eye. So they held kestrels and owls to be
sacrosanct in fact as well as in law, and made it their business
to see that no outsider harried them. Gallacher could have
summed up his personal hates in five words: foxes, rats,
rabbits, crows and cushies. He was equally vehement in
summing up his likes. Even of the sparrowhawk he had been
heard to exclaim: "Man, if the bird's killin' cushies it's leavin'
something else alane. . . ."

Dawdling along the south side of The Strip, Gallacher poked
in the hedgebottom tangles with his stick, for in the hardbitten, half-century farmer the nesting schoolboy still lived.
He was a hundred yards from the kestrels' tree, looking at a
partridge nest which contained ten eggs cunningly covered
with leaves and grass, when the dogs started to growl, warning
him of the approach of a stranger. Coming across the field
towards him was a man he didn't know. And he was carrying
a gun!

That put Gallacher's birses up for a start. Always a thrawn man, he was never uncivil without good reason; but when he was wound up he could sned thistles with his tongue. He was winding up now. Who was this who dared go traipsing over his ground with a gun, in the month of May, without so much as by-your-leave? The man came forward and spoke:

"Mr Gallacher? I saw you from the road. I wanted to speak to you. I'm the new keeper from ower by. I hope you'll excuse . . . ?"

Gallacher thawed out on the instant, glad he hadn't greeted the man with some hayfield snorter.

"Nell! Glen! Sit doon!" he said to the dogs. "Was it something?" He turned to the keeper. The man was wearing green tweeds, with fancy leather buttons on his jacket.

"Mr Gallacher"—the keeper leaned on his gun—"I've been here only a fortnight. I don't want you to think I'm butting in"—Gallacher was immediately on the defensive—"but I wondered if you kent there was—ah—certain—ah—vermin—aboot. . . ?"

"Vermin?" Gallacher was still civil, but leery. He had been friendly with the old keeper for twenty years. He had respected him. He was beginning to think he wasn't liking this one.

"Yes, vermin," said the keeper; "I just wondered. You know how it is! And I've the rearing field ower by. . . ."

"What vermin?" Gallacher was away out in front now, seeing the road ahead clearly.

"Ah! I was sure you widna ken." (How typical, thought Gallacher: the glib assumption that farmers were blind morons who couldn't see what was under their noses.) "It's hawks, Mr Gallacher. They're all over the place. So when I saw you here, I . . . There's one now!" he exclaimed suddenly, pointing above the cornfield, where a kestrel was balancing in the wind, with tail depressed, scanning the trembling green below.

"That!" Gallacher laughed. And when Gallacher laughed you could hear him three fields away. "Man, there's anither wan nae farther awa than ye could rin haudin' your braith, an' she's sittin' on six eggs this very meenit!"

"A nest? But these birds will play the dickens with your partridges. Believe me; I ken."

"D'ye tell me that?" Gallacher was derisive, but still feeling jocular.

"And my young phaisants; they'll be a sitting target. I've seen hawks aboot in the early morning."

"That'll be right." Gallacher was still civil.

The keeper was getting nettled. "But you don't seem to understand, Mr Gallacher. Hawks——"

"Man, I understaun fine," said Gallacher banteringly; "you don't like hawks! Funny thing is your predeceesor didna mind them a bit, an' he raired a pickle phaisants in his time."

"That's as may be, Mr Gallacher; but vermin's vermin, and it's my job to see——"

"Look!" Gallacher interrupted him; "maybe I don't understaun aboot vermin, but I understaun this. This is ma ferm. I'll worry aboot the pairtridges an' the hawks. There's twa pairs nestin' inside ma mairch fences, an' God help the man who lays a finger on them. He'll need it!"

"Mr Gallacher; I didna mean to be interferin'. But the farms hereaboots are breeding places for vermin, and I get——"

"So that's it!" Gallacher interrupted him again. "You've nae vermin o' your ain so you're itchin' for somebody else's! But who feeds your rabbits? An' your phaisants? Me and the likes o' me! An' rabbits tae me are the worst o' vermin."

"But . . ."

"But nothing! I'll gi'e ye a word o' advice at nae cost. Leave thur kestrels alane. An' the next time ye come spierin' for me leave that gun ahint! I'll cairry the guns aboot here. An' while we're on the subject ye'd best get that pole trap doon I see on the mair afore a wee bird cheeps tae the polis. Guid day tae ye!"

And Gallacher left abruptly.

"Noo, Wull, you shouldna mak bad bluid," said his wife when he told her about his "words" with the new keeper. "You're far ower quick wi' your tongue! The man was only daein' his job as he sees it."

"Bad bluid!" said Gallacher; "bad bluid is it! A man seeks me oot, a man I've never seen afore, tries tae run the ferm, wants tae shoot a' the hawks, an' I'm supposed tae say nothing!"

"There's ways o' daein' things, Wull, an' the man's a nee-bour."

"I thocht we'd seen the last o' that kind," said Gallacher. "But onyway, he can dae what the hell he likes on his ain grun', an' I'll attend tae mine. Look oot there noo!"

His wife left the sink, wiping her hands on her apron, and looked. On a big leet in the stackyard a kestrel had just pitched and scissored his wings. It was Yellow Foot, the cock from the nest in The Strip. The bird drooped a wing, lifted over a yellow-taloned foot, and clawed his ear; his head was slate-blue in the sun.

Gallacher turned to his wife. "Him an' his phaisants," he said. "I should've offered him a sovereign for every phaisant he could get in the nest an' ta'en a hauf-croon fae him for every moose. I could've made thirty poun' gin haytime!"

He saw the movement of wings through the window. "That's the wee man doon noo," he told his wife; "he'll ha'e anither moose. But I'm supposed tae scrub him an' let the mice mak meal o' the stacks!"

Yellow Foot, Gallacher's wee man, squeezed the life out of a fat vole on the straw-strewn ground, and flapped back to the leet-top with it in his claws, unaware that a farmer and an old-style keeper had been discussing his fate and, in a vague way, his ecology. The vole was his third from the Mossrigg stackyard that morning.

From the window, the farmer was watching him. Yellow Foot knew Gallacher as well as any wild falcon can ever know a man. He followed in his wake at ploughing time, hovered about at the tattie happing, flapped behind the binder at harvest time and hunted the stackyard all winter. Gallacher had erected a look-out perch for him: a stack prop stuck vertically in the ground; and Yellow Foot used it daily.

The little falcon pulled the head from his vole and swallowed it with much gaping and neck-stretching. Then he picked up the body and swallowed it too, a choking process with much grimacing. Gallacher was surprised; he thought the falcon would be carrying to his mate. He didn't know about the other voles. When Yellow Foot lifted from the leet the farmer drew in his chair to the kitchen table for his eleven o'clock tea.

Sixty feet above the roadside gate Yellow Foot began to hunt, hovering on fluttering wings with tail depressed and eyes scanning the ground. From his pitch he could see every movement in the grass below. His sharp eyes saw nothing in the stackyard, so he drifted thirty yards sideways and hovered again: he was now poised above the beeches of the hayfield hedge. Presently he saw movement in the clover, and when the movement became a dark shrew he closed his wings and swooped.

The shrew was scurrying fast towards the cover of the hedge-bottom, where lay a loosely rolled and twisted length of wire netting with grass growing through it. The arched-over end of it put Yellow Foot off his stroke, and he alighted in the clover with hooked beak open and tapered wings upheld. Seeing the shrew under the netting, he whisked forward with wings open and tried to force his way in after it. He pushed through the four-inch mesh of the outside layer, then tried to come out. When he couldn't force his way out he tried to force his way in, and in less than thirty seconds was hopelessly entangled. The more he struggled the worse his plight became, and soon he was held tightly, with head, wings and feet through different meshes. And, of course, he started to call.

Kek-kek-kek-kek-kek!

The first ears to hear, and heed, were the ears of Gallacher's big cat Scotch Jimmy, who came panthering through the hedge from the stackyard with tail-tip twitching. When Yellow Foot saw the cat he screeched louder than ever. He clicked his beak at Scotch Jimmy and clutched the wire strands with his talons. Jimmy pawed gingerly at the netting, sniffed from a safe distance, and mewed. He didn't like the wire, and he was a little dubious about the bird. So he sat down to ponder.

It was about then that Gallacher came out into the yard and heard the cries. He recognised the voice at once, and soon placed the direction; he knew the bird was calling in anger or alarm, and wondered why. Hurrying across the stackyard, led straight to the spot by the frantic cries, he shouldered through a narrow gap in the hedge and at once found the falcon with his cat-in-waiting. He picked up a clod and threw it at Scotch

Jimmy, who bolted with his tail up and his ears down. Then he turned to the bird.

Yellow Foot screeched at him, and when the big hand touched the netting he tried vainly to clutch it with a foot. Gallacher began to unroll the netting, then saw he could not do so without injuring the bird.

"Noo, hoo the hell did ye manage tae get in a predicament like that?" he asked the bird. Yellow Foot blinked his round, shining eyes and kekked at him. Gallacher pushed back through the hedge and hurried to the farmhouse for cutters.

"Come awa an' see this!" he called to his wife. "The wee man's caught in auld wire nettin' in the haidge ower there."

"The kestrel?" his wife asked.

"Aye, the kestrel," he said; "whit a helluva place tae dump wire. Where's your seecaturs?"

They went back to the hedge together, wife carrying a duster and farmer carrying the cutters. Gallacher knelt down and began snipping the strands. Soon he had Yellow Foot's head and one wing free. He put the duster over the bird in case he pecked, and snipped on with much care to free the yellow feet. He cut the bird loose at the cost of one tail feather, then groped under the duster to span the thrusting wings with his hands and manœuvre the legs between his fingers. When he had Yellow Foot securely gripped he rose and shook off the duster.

"Ye never thocht ye'd be this close tae a kestrel, noo, did ye?" he said to his wife.

"He's braw," she said. "Let him go noo. An' ye'd better shift that wire."

Gallacher removed one hand to fan open a wing so that his wife could see its pretty markings. Yellow Foot promptly freed a leg and clutched the hand with a foot. The needle-sharp claws pricked the farmer's big horny hand and squeezed. Gallacher laughed.

"Noo, that's gratitude!" he chided. He took the leg back between the fingers of his other hand, straightened it, and eased out the claws. He opened his hands, and Yellow Foot flashed into the air, shrilling abuse.

Gallacher held aside thorn branches to let his wife back through the hedge. He followed her—without the netting. . . .

Yellow Foot did not come to the stackyard for several days and Gallacher began to wonder if the bird had been seriously injured after all. Then, one morning, he saw him balancing on his look-out post with something under his feet, and knew that all was well.

What Yellow Foot had under his talons was a bright-eyed woodmouse, which he had clutched from the clover beyond the stackyard hedge. Its ribs were squeezed; its heart crushed; and there was dark blood on the tip of its snout. Gallacher watched while the bird grasped his prey with both sets of talons and launched from the post.

The morning was overcast, and birds were singing. Yellow Foot flew over the roadside hedge at twenty feet, and swerved when he saw a policeman on the verge, walking with his bicycle because it had a punctured tyre. The policeman looked up as the falcon swerved, and watched him flying low over the cornfield, low over the cows in the pasture, low over the next cornfield, then beating up towards The Strip to pitch in his calling tree in less than thirty seconds. Then he turned in at the Mossrigg road-end to mend the puncture at the farm.

Wree-wree-wree-wree-wree-wree! called Yellow Foot on his perch, with the woodmouse held in a foot. *Wree-wree-wree-wree-wree!* he called again, and transferred the mouse to his beak.

Wree-wree-wree-wree-wree-wree! his mate, Kree, replied, and hopped from her eggs. *Wree-wree-wree-wree-wree-wree!* she called, and flew out to join him.

Yellow Foot stood tall when Kree pitched beside him, and watched gravely while she bowed on the perch, with spread tail quivering in greeting. They said *wree-wree* to each other, softly; then Kree took the prey from her mate's blood-splashed beak and swallowed it with much blinking and head-shaking. Yellow Foot whetted his beak, looked about him, and slipped away sideways from the branch. Kree, with head skewed, watched him for some moments with one lustrous, far-seeing eye. When he had drifted out of sight beyond the trees, she shook herself and fell to preening her breast feathers. This was the time of day when she took a few minutes off from her brooding.

"Mornin'!" the policeman greeted Gallacher. "I see a hawk away across the road there. Ye'll ha'e tae be mindin' your chickens!"

"Wife!" Gallacher called through the door: "here's anither wan!" The tone was bantering. He liked the policeman.

The policeman laughed. "Oh, well," he said, "they're your chickens! I just thought I'd tell ye. The new keeper ower by was sayin'——"

"I ken what he was sayin'," Gallacher interrupted. "The place is hotchin' wi' vermin! He canny sleep at night for thinkin' aboot ma pairtridges. But did he tell ye aboot oor wee teet-a-teet?"

"Aye!" The policeman grinned slyly. "He did say something aboot a wee bit turavee. He canny understand ony man likin' vermin. He's sair doon on hawks, the man."

"This is a helluva joke!" Gallacher said; "when the law starts makin' excuses for gemkeepers. D'ye never read the Bird notices ootside your office? Whit d'they say aboot kestrels?"

"That's right enough. . . . But when a man's tryin' tae breed game. . . ."

"But nothin'!" Gallacher was mounted now, applying the spurs. "Gem! Gem! Gem! Every pauper between here an' hell, withoot wan shillin' tae rub agin anither, has got gem on the brain. A man wid think ye were a' big lairds or somethin'. Noo, there's a pole trap on the mair beyond Brockhurst. Ha'e ye seen it?"

"Aye!" the policeman was laughing; "but he says it's for craws! He says——"

"Craws! Craws, man! There never was a craw gotten in a pole trap yet. In ma faither's time a' I ever saw in them was hawks an' owls. An' that's what they're set for yet!"

"Oh, well," the policeman said: "it's your ferm, and your vermin. You'll ken your ain ken best. But when I get this puncture fixed I'll get on tae the pole trap. . . ."

"Aye! it's ma ferm a' right, though sometimes I begin tae wonder! Come on in man an' ha'e a cup o' tea. Geordie!" he bawled suddenly to the cattleman. "See if ye can mend this puncture while the polisman's hae'in' a bite."

Kree was raking her rump plumes, with one eye closed, when she was alerted by the piercing screams of her mate:

Kek-kek-kek-kek-kek-kek!

She launched away with a whicker of wings as Yellow Foot came pin-wheeling down, flattened out, and flashed towards the nest. He was above it, hovering with hanging feet, when Kree topped the pines: gold-tipped and blue-green in the hazed sunlight, and in a moment she was beside him, wing to wing, with yellow talons clutching at the marauder on the nest.

The magpie had sneaked in when Kree was preening, noting the vacant nest when he was flying home to his own. Now he was upended on a branch at nest level, with rainbow tail speared and ebony beak stabbing at an egg. He had already pierced one, and yellow yolk and scarlet blood were glueing on his beak; he had cracked the second, but before he could hole it the outraged falcons were upon him.

Now a kestrel will not, under ordinary circumstances, assault a magpie; nor is it fitted to do so. In The Strip, magpies and crows nested each year with the kestrels, obeying the unwritten law that you don't raid your neighbours. But such a truce is always uneasy; always liable to be broken under stress —or when the right kind of opportunity offers. The magpie had been tempted by opportunity; now he was ready to withdraw without a fight because he knew he was in the wrong.

But the kestrels had other ideas. They had no kind of understanding of truces or laws; they understood only a pattern of behaviour which was routine. The pattern had been broken; there was a magpie on the nest; so they went in to the attack, angrily yet circumspectly, for they knew they were dealing with a powerful and cunning enemy.

It was the magpie's willingness to retreat that gave the falcons their chance. As he turned to fly from the branch, Kree struck him on a wing, unbalancing him, and making him lose his grip on the air. While he was trying to catch hold again,

Yellow Foot took him on the face with his claws, blotting out one dark eye with a hind talon and clutching his neck in a foot. Such a grip the magpie could not shake off, but he had time to act before the talons choked out his life. And he acted.

He went right to earth, with the falcon riding him down. Kree hovered behind Yellow Foot, and pitched on the grass when the locked birds grounded. Yellow Foot released his grip during the landing fankle and flapped over to Kree to consider the next move. That gave the magpie his opportunity. With legs braced widely apart, tail fanned down in support, and beak presented like a rapier, he awaited the attack.

Kree flashed in but was met by a lightning stab of the magpie's beak; the blow hurt, and removed two feathers from her breast. Yellow Foot struck, and was met by a similar riposte which jarred his keel. Then, as if realising that one to one left the odds in the magpie's favour, they struck together. Kree recoiled as the magpie stabbed, but her mate flapped astride him again, with the old grip, and another claw sunk in the enemy's remaining eye. The magpie called *chock-ock* when the darkness came, and in the same instant Kree was on his back, clawing for a grip.

They clawed at him; they screamed; they buffeted him with their wings. But he was slow to crumple, and dragged them many yards before he stopped at last, with head bowed and beak pressed to earth. Together they flapped up, their fury spent, and flew to separate branches beside the nest. The magpie moved, ground-flapping and crawling, to seek refuge under a grass-grown briar; and there he was found, and chopped, by a fox when the moon highlight was bright in the eyes of Kree as she cuddled close her four sound eggs against the chill of the night.

The fight with the magpie changed the whole social pattern in The Strip by changing the outlook of the kestrels. Any magpie was, for them, the bird that had raided the nest, so a time of trial began for the hen magpie, now left to fend for her nestlings alone.

Each time she flew from The Strip on her foraging she was intercepted and harried by Yellow Foot, unless he was hunting more than two fields away. He attacked from above and behind, and sometimes he clawed feathers from her; but he was unable to injure her, or force her from The Strip. Stubbornly, she carried on feeding her chicks, fighting back at each assault and refusing to be intimidated. The harrying continued when she was feeding fledglings in the branches, until at last she was forced to take them further afield: to the dark pines of Cowther Wood nearly half a mile away. Yet she had no real cause for fear, for not once during his war with the magpies had Yellow Foot ever molested her chicks.

One moonless night, when the peewits were calling as they swept on humming wings over the trees, Kree felt movement under her and knew that her first chick had hatched. She slept fitfully for an hour afterwards, while the chick dried, cheetering; when she reached under her and tossed two unequal pieces of egg shell on the edge of the nest, the chick wriggled up into the warm feathers of her thighs. At daybreak she was brooding two downy chicks and two chipped eggs.

Yellow Foot flew in twice to the nest during the morning, and Kree, without rising, snatched a vole and a shrew from his beak, laying them beside her, on the outside of her breast. They were for her chicks. Yellow Foot made three more visits before the sun was red, bringing in two more voles and a black water shrew without a head, and these, too, Kree laid carefully in the nest. During the night the two remaining eggs hatched out, and when the sun rose again, frayed and crimson in the morning mists, she was heaving on four squirming, downy chicks which cheetered each time she moved.

She fed them at mid-morning, when dark clouds hid the sun and the trees were tossing in the wind. Standing aside from them, with a vole held under her feet, she pulled off small pieces of meat with her hooked beak, and, with a sideways tilt of her head, placed the morsels in their mouths. They cheetered as she fed them. When they drooped, with hunger satisfied, she picked up the remainder of the vole—a torn, bloody remnant— and gulped it whole. Then she settled down to brood.

During the next six days Yellow Foot brought thirty-two kills to his mate: fourteen voles, eight shrews, seven mice, one baby rabbit, one young rat, and one meadow pipit. In the early morning he flew right in to the nest with his kills; but during the day he called Kree to his tree and he passed the prey to her there.

Day after day he spent many hours hovering above the fields or the Mossrigg stackyard, hunting for his family. One day he killed a small bitch weasel in a lane. She was less than three ounces in weight, but savage, and bit him in the leg before she died. When he arrived back in The Strip, carrying her by the head, there was blood on one of his yellow legs and clotted feathers on his thigh. The body lay on the nest for a day, then was tossed out by Kree, who would not touch it.

Gallacher saw a lot of Yellow Foot in that week, perched in the stackyard or hovering above the cornfields on uplifted wings, and guessed the bird was busy with a family. Then, for three days, he did not see the little falcon at all. The fact registered suddenly, and he remarked to his wife:

"Come tae think o't; the wee man hisna been in the stackyard this twa-three days back. Must be on another beat. . . ."

But he wondered about it, and the following morning he visited The Strip to allay his vague fears. Yellow Foot at once flew up to circle overhead screaming, and Gallacher was put off. There was no sign of Kree but the fact did not strike him at the time and he left without misgiving. He didn't know the story of the twa-three days when Yellow Foot was absent from the stackyard.

It happened after dark, when owls were hooting in The Strip, and the night sky was smoorey, threatening rain.

Yellow Foot, roosting in a tall tree near the nest, heard stealthy footsteps on the ground, and lifted away when they passed beneath him. Presently, Kree heard them, too, and peered over the edge of the nest. Suddenly, boots struck the tree and branches began to shake, and Kree flashed from the nest to join Yellow Foot in the gloaming.

A man was climbing!

The falcons circled, screaming, flying high and fast, alarmed by the dark figure of the man at the nest. But the visit was brief. In less than a minute the man was climbing down again, and the birds dropped lower to watch. They heard the thud of his feet on the ground, then his footsteps hurrying away through

I

the trees. As soon as he was clear of The Strip, Kree circled down to the nest to find her four chicks cheeping and squirming, bunched together in a downy molehill. They were unharmed. Yellow Foot touched down for a brief moment, saw Kree straddle her chicks, and flew back to his roost; and both birds settled as though they had never been startled.

It is doubtful if Kree was capable of realising that she had three mice in the nest that had not been brought by her mate. In any case, she found them in the morning. She did not use them right away, for Yellow Foot came in with two fresh kills in fifteen minutes and she tore them up first. It was in the late afternoon that she used the mysterious mice—feeding two to her chicks and swallowing the third herself. Then she crouched on the nest, with her wings half-open, sheltering her chicks.

When Yellow Foot called to her later in the day, there was no answer. He called to her again and again; still she was silent. Puzzled, he flew to the nest with a vole in his beak, calling *wree-wree-wree*. Kree did not answer. She could not answer. She was dead: sprawled on the edge of the nest with eyes closed and slim talons clenched. Her chicks were huddled in the centre of the nest—dead. Yellow Foot dropped his vole in the nest, stared uncomprehendingly, then flew away to catch another. After he delivered the next one he returned to his roost and delivered no more. He knew.

Gallacher found them when he climbed to the nest—a mere routine visit—two days after he had checked The Strip for Yellow Foot. Like Yellow Foot, he stared at the dead bodies uncomprehendingly. Yellow Foot circled above him, swearing, the pattern of his life restored by the presence of the man at the nest. Gallacher tossed Kree's body to the ground, certain she had not been shot, convinced she had died a natural death.

Until he found the button—a leather button, with a small piece of green tweed attached—caught on a sharp sliver halfway down the tree. Gallacher looked at it long, for he had seen that button before, and knew where to find the jacket from which it had been torn.

The Foumart of Ravenscraig Wood

HE came hurrying down through the barred and chequered moonlight of Ravenscraig Wood—sinuous, darting, rippling; leaping from mossed stump to black-veined boulder; pattering along the brashed trunks of fresh windfalls: a giant weasel with yellow cheeks, pale lips and ears edged with white, masked and dark-furred, with bottle brush tail. And, by all accounts, he had no right to be there.

But he *was* there; he was no wraith. However, being a polecat—called by some foul marten or foumart, to distinguish him from his relative the pine, or sweet, marten—there was a doubt about his pedigree, for the nearest true polecats were supposed to be in Wales, several hundreds of miles away. Many people maintain that there are no true polecats left in Scotland; others, more careful, reserve judgement. This question of right polecats and wrong polecats, which seems to me to be what it amounts to, is worth looking at for a moment.

There may well be polecats left in Caithness; if there are, they'll be full-blooded specimens. There *are* polecats in other parts of Scotland, which may be the right kind or the wrong kind. But there are polecats on Mull about which there is no doubt at all: they are the descendants of tame polecats, called polecat-ferrets, which became feral many years ago on that island. These polecats are rejected by the systematists because their lineage runs the wrong way, as it were. But, for the life of me, I cannot see why a polecat—because his ancestors once lived in hutches—is any less a polecat, than a Highland wildcat is a wildcat because one of his ancestors contracted a liaison with a domestic tabby.

The systematists used to claim that they could tell a real wild polecat from a feral descendant of the polecat-ferret by certain conformations of the bones of the skull. Now this is rejected. It is thought today that facial markings may be a true guide to identity. But it seems to me that a polecat that looks like a polecat, acts like a polecat, and breeds polecats which look like polecats, is a polecat for all practical purposes. The argument becomes academic if the polecat happens to raid your henhouse; real or *ersatz*, the result is the same.

The big dog polecat of Ravenscraig could have been real or an impostor, but I am not concerned about him here, for when he reached the drag-road through the timber he had to go sneaking up to the woodsman's hut and get himself caught in a gin trap—the same kind of trap which was responsible for killing off his ancestors over the greater part of Scotland. He hissed and chattered when the steel teeth gripped his paw, and his cries attracted the woodsman, who came out with a lantern in one hand and a faggot in the other and killed him with a sharp blow on the head. As I say, we are not concerned with him, though there was much argument about what kind of beast he was.

This story is about his mate.

Foumart, the bitch polecat of Ravenscraig, was smaller than her mate, which is the way of it with the true weasels. She was less than two pounds in weight, and barely twenty inches from her nose to the tip of her tail. In colour she was like him—dark purple-brown guard hairs overlaying pale buff underfur; but the patches between eyes and ears were less yellow and more grey, so that her masking was not so striking. Though less powerful, she was no less savage.

For some months she had been running with her mate, shifting ground regularly, and travelling by way of the glens; they had put range after range of mountains behind them. Now Foumart was plump, being heavy with young, and her wanderings were over for the present. She had already made her nest in a rock cleft, at 1,200 feet, in a birch thicket above Ravenscraig. It was a warm nest of dried grasses and rushes, which she had bitten off, or scraped together, and carried in her mouth.

The moon spotlighted her as she sat on the rock above her lair, in upright weasel pose, with bushy tail quivering; she was listening. Her breast was dark; she was more like a small wolverine than a big weasel. Her questing ears—supersensitive and highly selective—heard the hoof-swish of hinds among the trees; the light tread of a hare in the brushwood far up the hillside; the scurrying of voles in the deep of the heather; the claw-scrape of a cock capercaillie as he shuffled on his high pine roost in the wood. Foumart dropped to all fours and glided from the rock.

She crossed the hillside in a series of darts and scurries, sometimes bounding, but freezing every now and again to sit, with head up, listening. The moonlight did not betray her. She made use of every tussock, and heather clump, and pile of brushwood to conceal her movements, and when she sat bolt upright to listen she was just another dead, weathered piece of stick. The hillside was cleared forest, laned from glen to heights with layered branches—bleached, lichened, brittle. Foumart rippled over them, glided round them, insinuated her muscular weasel-body through them; she made no more noise than a vole might have made.

Her vision was poor, but her ears and nose were acutely sensitive, tuned to every nuance of sound or scent; she could have hunted blind. So she came on the curlew, brooding her four eggs in a wet, tussocky, hoof-marked lane between layered lines of brushwood. The bird was sleeping, with her long beak laid over her back. Foumart, hearing a movement as she burrowed her beak more comfortably into her feathers, twisted in her tracks and pattered towards the nest.

The curlew wakened when the polecat was almost on top of her. What she saw was a bristling fury, flashing white teeth. She knew fox and stoat, hedgehog and wildcat, but not this terrible grinning weasel. She leaped backwards even as Foumart's teeth snatched feathers from her neck, and lifted away with wild swish of wings, open-beaked and terrified, to throw about the sky in panic. Other curlews joined her, sweeping across the moonlit sky in shadowy flight, and their frantic cries could be heard by the woodsman in his hut beside the forest road.

Ignoring the bedlam she had set loose, Foumart spat feathers and pounced on an egg. She was smelling strongly of musk, its potency increased by her excitement: the musk-taint that is the mark of the weasels, and which is most powerful and overwhelming in the polecat. Cracking the first egg with her teeth, she bit through shell and membrane, shaking her head like a terrier with a rat, and ate the chick and its attached yolk-sac in a kind of frenzy. The second egg she opened more deliberately, spitting out the last fragment of brittle shell before she ate chick and yolk-sac without haste. Then, after sniffing at the two remaining eggs, she licked her forepaws methodically and washed her ferret-face like a cat.

Now she began to weave about, darting this way and that on her short legs, deceptively swift, supple as an eel: a weasel in every line of her, yet badger-like—seeking. . . . She knew what she was seeking, and she found it: a hole under an old, rotted root, corked by long weathering and parasites. After wriggling into the hole, and out again, she returned to the nest and rolled away one of the eggs under her chin, tossing it forward with her nose when it became lodged in a tussock. She pushed the egg into the hole, and went back for the second one. This, too, she rolled along and poked into the hole. She went in after it, squirmed about inside, then came out, shook herself, and glided away towards Ravenscraig wood.

The vast wood was still in the revealing moonlight, damp and balsamy-fragrant, and, to human ears, silent. But to Foumart—gliding, bouncing, weaving round mossed stumps and running with muffled tread over the soft ground carpet— it was not silent; for above her own breathing and the whisper of her pads, which she could hear, there came to her ears the myriad sounds of the night: tread of rabbit and hare, mouse-squeak, the deep breath of a hind, the snort of a ewe, and the noise made by the ruffling of a woodpigeon's wings on a branch high overhead.

Through shadowy, light-chequered lanes of trees she leaped and ran—into old timber, unkempt, bearded with lichens, mossed and brooding—an eerie place, owl-haunted—where roebuck and fox trod their secret trails, where gaunt trunks of oak and corded ash, shorn and splintered to their waists by storm and lightning, crouched scarred and festooned: moulder-ing relics of a forgotten age. The polecat drifted through, wraith-like, flank to flank with her shadow, past the tremendous earthworks at a badger sett, and followed the well-marked trail of the brocks to the drag-road.

She ran the rutted drag-road, with its chips and sawdust and scattered bark peelings, till she reached the tiered log-piles near the woodsman's hut. And up she had to go on to the first criss-crossed stack; up, then down again, then on to the next. She climbed well, but not expertly—not as expertly as a marten—and came down like a cat. She was on the stack by the woodsman's hut, weaving in circles, badger-like, sniffing, when it came to her on the air—musk-smell on a flaff of wind. It was the musk-smell of the dead dog polecat.

He was hanging by the neck from a pine branch that reached below the gable wall of the hut. Foumart couldn't see him, but she could smell him. Probably she knew what it meant. She snarled noiselessly, pattered back over the logs, and dropped to earth by the way she had come. She avoided the hut and, skirting the sawdust drifts on the slope to the glen, bounded down into the shadows.

Down there the Slainte rushed, broken and white-crested, over splintered ledges. The banks were rocky and steep, drip-ping water, and draped with woodrush. Foumart leaped and slid down the steep to the lip of the burn. With forepaws on a stone, and head weaving in circles, she looked across the rioting water, and knew the current was too strong for her. She would have crossed in an emergency, for she had no fear of water and was a strong swimmer; but there was no

emergency. Back-tracking from the stone, she turned away
upstream to the bridge and crossed by the parapet.

The moon was now slanting down the sky; soon it would be
setting. Foumart raced from the glen, rippled across the forest
road at the top, and was faced by the high deer fence, which
was netted half-way to the top against rabbits and hares. She
ran along the bottom of the fence, to left and right, padding at
the netting with her forepaws, then, realising there was no way
through, she climbed up it as if it was a ladder, gripping the
meshes with her claws, and toppled over the holding strand
into the planting of young Norway spruces.

The spruces were roe-high, crowded and interlacing, densely
undergrown with thick grass, ling, bell heather and seedling
birches; the undergrowth was riddled with vole creeps. To
move silently in such cover was almost impossible, even for
one as stealthy as Foumart, and the swish of her as she forced
her way through the smother, parting the grass with her face,
was heard by a moor owl on her nest in the heather twenty-
five yards away. The owl hearkened, blinking her yellow and
black eyes; she knew no vole was running there. But she was
spared a death-grapple in the tall heather that night, for the
sounds moved away from her and passed beyond her hearing.

Foumart cleared the young spruce planting and reached the
edge of a roundel of mature trees where the ground cover was
thin. There, in a few minutes, she pounced on two voles, killing
them by a nip on the skull behind the ear. But she did not eat
them. Instead, she snatched them up in her jaws and went
leaping back down through the heavy cover of the planting,
not troubling to conceal the line of her going. The moor owl
on her nest long-necked in alarm, but again the sounds died
away, and she settled back to brooding her well-filled eggs.

Haste was now driving the bitch polecat. She did not stop
to sit up and listen. Down to the Slainte she slipped and leaped,
and across the parapet of the bridge; then up past the wood-
piles and into the deepening gloom of Ravenscraig. When she
left the trees the moon had set, and when she crossed the open
hillside, running the brushwood lanes, she was invisible. The
curlews were still keening about their ruined nest, but she
ignored them. The ground gloom was now deep enough to

hide deer moving in line at twenty paces; beyond the pine-tops of Ravenscraig the sky was silvering. Foumart padded to her den in the rock cleft and squeezed in to her nest.

But not to stay! She dropped her voles in a side pocket of the rock-hole and came out again at once, breathing with lips parted and smelling of musk. Away through the birch scrub she scampered, swallowed in the ground gloom: the gloom that meant nothing to her because her nose and ears were better than her eyes. And curlews, grouse and peewits rose calling at intervals to betray her route.

This time she was not hunting aimlessly; she knew where she was going. Within fifteen minutes of leaving her den she was crossing the forest road again to the Slainte, but this time far out from the wood, in the open deer forest, where the wide flats by the burn were boggy and there were many small pools. There the soft peat was printed with the seals of otters, and deer came to scrape for a bite when the snow lay deep on the tops.

The polecat knew where she was going; she also knew what she was after. Out in the bog she padded, cat-footed, skirting the biggest pools, wading through the small and shallow. Her pattering feet plashed lightly in the puddles. All the time her ears and nose were alert for scent and movement.

Suddenly there was a *plop!* Then—snap! She had a frog. Snap-snap! She had another. They lay squirming, not dead. Foumart gathered them, gripping them by the thighs, then weaved from the bog with them dangling from her mouth. She had disabled them, without killing them: not like the queen wasp, who anaesthetises caterpillars with her venom, but as the mole with earthworms, paralysing them with a bite.

Back at her den in the rock, she laid her frogs beside the dead bodies of the voles; and again she came out—this time to curl up on the entrance ledge and lick her fur. She licked and dozed till the sun cleared the sgurr behind Ravenscraig, gilding the great fang of Ben Dearg, turning the pines across the Slainte to pillars of flame and the pools on the flats to liquid fire. Out on the slope the blackcocks strutted, in brilliant crimson wattle, with ebony plumage glinting metallic purple, and when the Ben Dearg eagle came over low, banking steeply in the sun, his crown was touched with gold.

Foumart rose and crawled into the cleft. There was a dragging ache in her belly. Her time had come.

Five kits were born to the polecat in the nest in the cleft—five pale, ferret-like kits who made incessant demands on her breasts. Day after day she lay up with them, leaving them only for brief periods to void and drink, and in those first days she lived on the frogs and voles she had laid by before her kits were born.

On the fifth day, leaving them warmly curled up in the nest, she bounded down the brushwood lane to the root-hole where she had stored the curlew's eggs. The chicks in the eggs were chill and slightly tainted, but she ate them, leaving only the shells and yolk-sacs. This was the last of her stored food. To-morrow she would have to hunt. But she had left the ground near her den little disturbed, so that she would not have to range far from her helpless kits.

During the next week she hunted Ravenscraig Wood, the cleared hillside and the glen of the Slainte, rarely ranging more than half a mile from the den in any direction. She killed rabbits, leverets, voles, a brood of young peewits, a slow-worm and a lizard. Her hunger was great and she fed heavily; but she was a wasteful hunter by human standards, killing more than she needed and sometimes not returning to a prey which she had only half eaten.

So man speaks of Foumart's kind as bloodthirsty, ravening Nimrods who strike terror into the heart of every living thing. Foumart was indeed a killer—savage, implacable, ruthless; she held nothing sacred. But what hunter does? What she could catch and hold she would attack; what she could kill she killed. She was merciless, as all the hunters of the wild are merciless, which means that sentiment was something unknown to her. And she killed more than she could eat, which is the cardinal sin, though not peculiar to polecats. But it would be wrong to accuse her of spreading terror far and wide on her range. Her victims knew fear when she was there in front of them—bristling, leaping, reaching for their throats: they did not spend their lives thinking about her.

Beyond all that she was a devoted and jealous mother, ready

to fight to the death in defence of her kits, ready to challenge any trespasser even when they were not directly threatened. Put to the test, she would have faced man.

She came home one morning, when her kits were a fortnight old, with two voles in her belly and one in her jaws. She laid the vole in a corner of the den and came out to the ledge in front to lick her fur, and rest, for she was now liking spells away from her demanding family. It was when she was tongueing the fur of her breast that she saw the fox.

He came dawdling through the birch scrub, with no nonsense in his head and a hen grouse in his jaws: a big Highland dog fox, with brown legs and an enormous brush, travelling home with prey for his cubs. But his route was taking him below the rock where crouched the polecat, and the polecat immediately saw him as a threat to her kits. That meant she was ready to carry the war to the enemy.

Poor bewildered *sionnach*! The first he knew about the polecat was when she landed beside him, hissing and bristling. He whisked aside, drawing in his brush, but she came after him, *tissing* and chattering, reaching for his heels. That disconcerted him, for he was sensitive about his pads and his big tendon, so he ran twenty paces and stopped to ponder. But he was given no time to ponder, because she came bounding up to him again, flashing her needle teeth, and snapping at his feet.

Now he began to feel nettled. Though she was bigger than any weasel he had ever seen, he recognised her as one of the clan. He held weasels in contempt. Big though this one was, he was thirteen times her weight and could have broken her back with his long jaws. He had a feeling, however, that he was somehow trespassing, so he was prepared to be ordered away.

But, presently, he changed his mind. The more he retreated, the more she hustled him, running at him and snapping at him: a bristling, explosive stink-weasel with the hair of her tail on end. For three hundred yards he retreated before her without losing his temper; but his own den was now only a quarter of a mile away, uphill, and his anger increased as the distance grew less. Foumart was pushing close to the point where she would be the trespasser.

At the half-way stage the big reynard had had enough of dancing and side-stepping like a big dog being harassed by a puppy. But he could not fight back with his mouth full, so he dropped his bird behind a boulder and turned to face her. And Foumart realised that the time had come to quit.

He was a master of the quick chop and flick of the paw, and he upended her once with a shrewd stroke. But, before he could get his long teeth near her, she somersaulted aside and clear. He followed her, poking at her and snapping at her back; he headed her and chopped at her mask, forcing her to turn; and once his teeth clashed so close that they pulled dark hairs from her rump. Foumart realised now that she was fighting for her life, and when she found a cavity under a rock she wasted no time scuttering into it. Even at that, his teeth almost closed like a trap on her bushed tail.

Now the reynard was satisfied; but Foumart was not. It was all against her fierce nature to miss an opportunity of striking back. Hardly had she drawn in her tail than, snake-like, she had turned about, and her masked face was at the entrance to the hole. The fox's muzzle was close, and she tried to bite him. Fortunately her teeth closed on air. If she had bitten him he would have tried to dig her out, or he might have waited for her coming out, and chopped her. But he was not bearing a grudge; neither his hide nor his pride was hurt; so he went away, picked up his grouse, and trotted to his den high above Ravenscraig.

Foumart peeped out when she heard him leaving; but it was some time before she came right out to go bounding down the brushwood lane to her kits.

The day was the twenty-eighth of May; the time six o'clock in the morning. The mists were sweeping, the sky grey with brooding clouds, the heather beaded with moisture. In the heart of a heather clump a little roe fawn was lying, with slim legs gathered under him and jet muzzle against his flank; he was twelve hours old, twice suckled. In the mist less than a hundred yards away his mother was standing over her second fawn. Of the buck there was no sign.

Foumart came pattering downhill from the heights with the

wind on the side of her muzzle; up there she had killed a grouse and eaten half the breast. So she had no hunger for food. The roe fawn, however, was in her path—right on the line she was travelling. She could not see him; she could not hear him; and it is unlikely she could smell him. But she had to run right on to him. . . .

The contact with the warm, breathing, quivering thing was enough for her. She flew at the fawn's throat, which was her way with prey too big to be killed by a single bite behind the ear. The prick of her needle teeth brought from him a wild cry, and he sprackled to his feet, staggering and trying to shake her from his neck. His struggles stung Foumart to savage fury, and she bit at him, and clawed at him with her feet. But his cries brought the doe.

She came up boldly, with forelegs flailing, but her first assault on the polecat was with her head. She butted Foumart from her hold on the fawn, sending her spinning into the heather, then followed up with fore-hooves dabbing. One blow from them would have smashed the polecat's spine, or stove in her ribs; but Foumart, realising the kind of wrath she had called down on herself, kept rolling and twisting in the heather, and leaping away when she could. By a miracle she escaped the pounding hooves, and the doe, more concerned about her fawn than about vengeance, presently broke off the chase. When she pranced back to her fawn, who had by then fallen terrified in the heather, Foumart scampered downhill as fast as her short legs could take her.

But there was still the buck—savage, dauntless, and a perfect fighting machine—and when he saw Foumart leaping in the heather he bounded after her. Probably, although he had not seen the assault, he was able to associate the fleeing polecat with the plight of the fawn. He attacked with the utmost savagery, pounding at Foumart as if he would stamp her right into the ground, and once he almost caught her off guard by prodding at her with his dirks. She felt the antler-tip graze her back, but she managed to wriggle away. Then, when she was dazed, panting and almost blind with rage and fear, she rolled into an old fox den—safe. The buck stamped round the hole for some time, and she could hear the hisses and hog-grunts of him, but, presently, the rage cooling in him, he too went away and she was left in peace.

Though uninjured, she was shaken. When she returned to her den she curled up with her kits and slept with them for some hours, nursing them as she slept. For the remainder of the day she lay away from them, near the den mouth, going in at intervals to nurse them, and it was long after midnight before she was pained by hunger and driven out to hunt.

The night was moonless, and the sky clear; the stars winked faintly. At that latitude there was no real darkness, and the polecat was a moving shadow on the hill. For an hour she hunted the ridge-top, catching only a vole, and then, when she was sitting up, in her listening pose, she heard sounds that were new to her. They came to her, now clear, now muted, with intervals of silence: cat-hisses and *ruckety-cooing* and a sound like the beating of wings. Foumart dropped to all fours and rippled down towards the sounds without further listening.

There were eleven blackcocks on the Lek. In full sunlight they would have been sable and ebony and iridescent purple, with bright crimson wattles; in the gloaming they were dark, indistinct shapes, visible only to the polecat in movement. Foumart bellied up to a pile of brushwood on the fringe of the Lek. The branches were grey and brown and silver, crusted with lichens; Foumart crouched among them and was invisible.

Some of the blackcocks were singing on their stances, with chests inflated; others were crowing, leaping as they crowed. The two birds nearest the crouching polecat were threatening each other, side-stepping face to face with lyre tails spread, then leaping at each other with hard slap of wings. They were unaware of Foumart's presence. She gathered her hindlegs when they began to side-step towards her, and when they were within striking distance she leaped to the attack.

She landed on the back of the nearer bird, clawing and biting, and he went down, hissing and flapping wildly, with her teeth in his neck. The second bird flapped up and away, in swift down-curved flight, towards Ravenscraig Wood. The other birds on the Lek, not knowing what was afoot, long-necked for a moment then returned to their jousting and crooning; perhaps they thought the blackcock across the Lek, beating his wings in death, was merely engaged in formal combat. Only when Foumart began dragging her prey to the shelter of the brushwood did they realise something was amiss; then they flew up, one after the other, and disappeared in the gloaming.

In the brushwood pile, Foumart tore glossy feathers from the breast of her still-twitching prey, and gorged herself on the dark flesh of the breast. When she was sated, her mask was crimsoned with blood. Afterwards, she had a mind to take her prey with her, so she grasped the body by the bared keel and padded away with it, holding her head high to prevent it from dragging. But the wings snagged in the layered branches, or trailed under her feet, so in the end she hid the body under another pile of brushwood and went home without it. She had a notion that she would return to it.

That same day, at mid-morning, when larks were singing and cuckoos calling, the keeper saw the bloody feathers of the blackcock on the Lek, and wondered. Then his terrier found the half-eaten body in the brushwood, and he wondered still more.

Right away he thought of fox, which is what anyone would have thought of at first glance, but he was puzzled as to why any fox should eat half a blackcock in the open, then leave the rest, at the time of big cubs and big appetites. He rejected wildcat for the same reason; the cat would surely have carried the prey away. Then he thought of stoat, and decided it must be stoat, though still taken with the idea of an improvident or wasteful fox. Being a man who liked the quickest way of finding out about such things, he took a gin from his game-bag and set it beside the carcase of the blackcock. When he left, he was still wondering how the bird had died.

Foumart left her den while the sun was still red, and hunted the height in the purple shadows of the afterglow. She scuttered this way and that, sitting up every now and then to listen, without once hearing any sound to interest her; and when she turned downhill at last, remembering the blackcock, the last of the light—tenuous gold and apple-green and saffron—was gathered behind the mountains of the west. It would fade; it would creep along the line of the peaks; but it would not be extinguished.

She went down in great bounds, no longer hunting by stealth because she knew there was food where she was going. The crackling of rotten branches halted her suddenly while her prey was still a long way off, and she sat up, turning an ear to the sound, to place it. A mountain hare, lying downwind of her, closed his twitching nostrils on her taint and went crashing away in the gloom, but she kept her ear on the lesser sound which had greater meaning for her. Ignoring the panic flight of the hare she resumed her hurried scamper down the slope.

Her taint reached the brushwood pile before her, for she was running down the wind, and when she was twenty yards from the spot the crackling suddenly stopped. That meant she was expected. She approached stealthily now, and slowly, edging round the wind. Her ears could tell her nothing, so she was seeking answers with her nose. When she got the scent she bristled, for the scent was fox!

He was caught fast by a hindfoot in the keeper's gin, and had been crashing in the brushwood in his attempts to drag it away. In his plight he was in no mood to be chivvied by any polecat, so he showed her the colour of his teeth, which were stained with his blood. Whether Foumart knew it or not, he was the same big dog fox who had chopped at her after she had chased him from her den; trapped to a prey not his own on his first foray of the night.

The blackcock was still where she had left it, except that the keeper had wedged it down. Foumart glided in to retrieve it, prepared to defy the fox, but he chopped and snarled at her so savagely that her bold spirit was daunted. In his fury he bit at the restraining gin till he broke his tusks, then he lunged out at the circling polecat. Foumart knew then she was courting death if she tried to reach her bird, so she snarled at him, then glided away, leaving him to be knocked on the head by the keeper in the morning.

She was in Ravenscraig Wood, running in the damp ground gloom under the pines, when the light behind the mountains had spread half-way towards the point of sunrise. She had killed two beetles, which she had eaten, and a weasel, which she had hidden against necessity, and the hunger was gnawing at her.

Right down to the drag-road, then along the drag-road to the deer-fence gate, she hunted; then into the old timber of Ravenscraig, where she weaved about, darting and freezing in the muffled gloom. No rabbit or vole was moving, and she did not yet know of the warren on the far side of the timber. Back down to the drag-road she padded, sliding the last six feet sideways down the mouldy bank. In a wheel rut she paused to scratch an ear with a hindfoot. The light was becoming stronger minute by minute.

Foumart shook herself vigorously, crossed the road, and turned along the top of the steep slope to the Slainte, moving, with rump arched, in shuffles and scurries; and again you would have had the impression of a small badger running. She was homing, but still hunting, so she heard the sound clearly and reacted instantly. It came from ahead, and downhill—low-pitched, intimate, almost breathless: the *tooking*, vaguely owl-like, of a hen capercaillie.

Now the polecat moved with consummate stealth; silent and deadly. Forward and downhill she stalked, bellying low, creeping from mossed stump to silver fir and spruce, ever manœuvring to keep obstacles before her to conceal her approach. Twice she dislodged pebbles which bounced with minute clatter downhill, but the caper merely blinked without turning her head. And, presently, Foumart was less than nine feet from her, slightly above and crouched behind the thick stem of a tall Norway spruce.

The hen capercaillie had three chicks wriggling under her and three struggling in splitting shells. The polecat couldn't yet see her, which is not surprising, for her plumage of black and white and buff and grey matched the withered leaves and dark twigs around her. But, feeling the chicks under her, she kept calling to them, so the polecat could place her by hearing. And, of course, she was very broody, which meant she had to recognise danger before she believed it, and be threatened before she moved.

Foumart gathered herself, padding for maximum thrust, and in two swift, unerring leaps was astride the capercaillie on

K

the nest. The great bird—the biggest grouse in the world—
exploded from her nest, scattering eggs and chicks down the
slope. Huge and powerful, with a tremendous wing-stroke, she
had no difficulty in launching into the air even with a polecat
attached to the feathers on the side of her chest. She did not
rise up; she went straight out from the face of the slope. And
took the polecat with her.

That strange, terrible flight lasted perhaps two seconds, for
Foumart had only a mouthful of feathers and, being airborne,
could not bore in for a better bite. She was carried aloft,
dangling, spinning, with the feathers twisting in her teeth. She
could not have released her grip even if it had occurred to her.
But the feathers ripped out with the strain, and when the
capercaillie was over the Slainte, twenty-five feet above the
rioting water, feathers and polecat parted company with her.

Kicking and spinning, Foumart fell: down, down, down,
into the brawling Slainte, which at that point was deep. She hit
the water with only a slight splash—a splash no greater than a
leaping fish would have made—but the shock stunned her; so
when she bobbed to the surface again, several yards downstream in the deep pool, her feeble, instinctive kicking could
not prevent her from being carried away, choking and spinning,
on the smooth current.

Once clear of the pool, she was tossed and thrown and
buffeted by the broken water, sucked under in the deep
channels then emerging, coughing with the water in her lungs,
to be rolled and battered in the rapids. She fought for her life,
but the first stunning plunge had left her at the mercy of the
water, and she was half drowned before her brain could direct
her legs to swim. So she was carried down and down, under the
deer fence and past the keeper's cottage, then through a narrow
gorge, to be washed at last on to a pebbly sand-spit, and left
there: battered, sodden and dead.

But that was not the end of her. Her body had to suffer the
final indignity. The following afternoon the keeper found her,
and carried her to his vermin board, and with a two-inch nail
he nailed her up by the neck beside the frayed, mummified and
skeletal corpses of stoats and weasels, who were her kin.

Haverin' Harry's Ghosts

HAVERIN' HARRY drained his third dram and wraxed himself out of the chair by the fire. The neat Standfast whisky, helped by the blazing logs, was already doing things to his head. He smacked his lips appreciatively and rubbed his straggling ginger moustache with the back of a calloused hand.

"That's a gran' dram, Alec," he said to the forester.

"Aye!" the forester laughed. "I made it masel'!"

Harry turned up his coat collar, pinned the lapels together, and walked to the door.

"The tree, Alec . . ." he began.

"It's in the lobby," the forester said. "But, sharely, Harry, you're no' thinkin' o' walkin' across the mair on a nicht like this?"

"Hiv tae!" Harry said, in the clipped way he had when the dram was on him. "Promised Mick it gin shuttin' time. Wee lassie wants it the nicht. Three miles is nothin'."

The six-foot Norway spruce was standing against the

grandfather clock in the hall. Harry picked it up and the forester opened the front door. The wind hit them in the face, rippled under the carpet and started the lamp shade swinging wildly. Fine snow swirled into the hall.

Harry squeezed out into the night and Alec slammed the door at his back with a hurried "Good night!"

On the road, the snow was deep, drifted and frozen. The stars flickered with icy brilliance. Powdery snow, sharp as sand, was being driven by the wind in stinging clouds. Harry lowered his head and trudged down the lane from the forester's cottage.

He turned left at the moor road, and for two hundred yards had the shelter of the tall, gloomy spruces of Glencryan Wood; but once clear of the trees he was at the mercy of the gale. It had mile on mile of open moor to gust and shriek over.

The wind staggered Harry sideways, almost tearing the whipping spruce from his oxter. Harry biased his weight to counter the gusts, and managed to hold the middle of the road, with his boots crunching on the hard snow.

He was a small man, but wiry. His clothes were oddments, second-hand and threadbare. His moustache was stained with nicotine. He had a slight, tapering chin, high cheekbones and a protruding lower lip.

They called him Soo-mooth to his face, and Haverin' Harry behind his back. In the vernacular he was "no' verra richt". Unkind people were blunter and said he wasn't all there, which means he was not right in the head. But they all had to admit he was a good workman, who didn't need watching, and who could turn his hand to anything: fencer, ditcher, trapper, ruck builder, stack thatcher, pig sticker, castrator of tup lambs, and drummer-up for the luggers at the quarry.

Still, he wasn't quite right. The higher-ups said he was M.D. And they didn't mean a doctor of medicine.

Harry, balanced on the wind, began to sing *The Soldier's Song*—a great favourite with him—to help him into better pace; but the wind had the last word. It tore the words from his lips and thrust him aside with a giant's hand.

Suddenly he halted, leaning into the wind, and shaking his head to clear the mist of alcohol from his brain.

A little way ahead, to his right, was the water hole known to the locals as The Murderer's Pound. Harry had passed it hundreds of times a year, by day and night, without ever giving much thought to its grim history. There, seventy years ago, a shepherd had found the body of a woman named Jean, in the deep water, with weights on her feet; and, beside her, the bodies of her two dogs, which had been poisoned before being thrown into the water.

The place, inevitably, was supposed to be haunted. The old folks had it that, on certain nights, Jean walked the moor, with her two dogs by her side and the weights clanking at her feet. There were even those who claimed to have seen her. And some of the old ones would never go near the place after midnight.

As I say, Harry had never thought much about the story before. But, on this night, he did think about it, for on the edge of the pound a white figure was standing, clear-cut against the dark saugh bushes on the verge, with white draperies flapping in the gale.

Harry's head cleared at once. He looked again at the spectre. There was no doubt about it; it was the figure of a woman, with her white robes flapping in the wind. Harry felt the hair creeping on the back of his neck. He would have retraced his steps, but that would have meant turning his back on the apparition.

For some moments he just stood there; then, screwing up his courage, he leaped the roadside ditch into the snowed-up heather, and stumbled and floundered on a wide detour. The wind buffeted him, and the snow packed his boot-heads, but he scrambled forward, with the warm sweat breaking on him, never taking his eyes from the white shape by the pound.

When he was two hundred yards beyond the pound he stumbled back to the road. Once there, he ran for three hundred before he stopped, gasping for breath, to look over his shoulder. He could see nothing: just a black-and-white landscape, smoored with fine wind-blown snow. There was no sign of life. Perhaps he had imagined the whole thing. They were for ever telling him he couldn't stand his dram. Perhaps . . .

The hair on his neck began to creep again.

What was he hearing now? Surely his ears and his eyes

couldn't both play tricks on him inside ten minutes? Harry stopped breathing to listen.

"Clank! Clank!" The sounds were muffled, but real; no trick of wind or ears this time. Harry stared into the scrub beyond the roadside ditch, and . . . Yes! There was movement there, all right, and, for a moment, he could have sworn he saw the horned one himself. Then, unmistakably, he heard the clank of metal on hard rock.

That was just about all Harry could take. He was in a panic. Then, even as he ran away, he saw them—the eyes! Green and luminous they were: the eyes of two beasts in the gloom of the scrub. Dogs! Jean's dogs! So he hadn't been imagining anything. Harry, hanging on to his spruce, ran until he collapsed with near-bursting lungs.

When Harry arrived at the village pub he was in a cold sweat and as white as the apparition he had just seen. The pub was closed, but the lights were still on, so Harry went round to the teetotaller's entrance and knocked.

The voice of Mick, the barman, asked: "Who's there?" Harry said: "Harry," and Mick drew the bolts and opened the door.

"Man, Harry, I was beginnin' tae think . . ." he began, and stopped. Staring at Harry, he bolted the door again. Harry staggered through to the lounge bar and threw himself into a seat by the fire.

Four men were already seated there: Gallacher of Mossrigg Farm, where Harry often worked; Jock Simpson, the fencer; Big Weellum, the roadman; and Pate, the moocher, with nails like a hawk's talons and eyes as bright as a jackdaw's.

Harry threw down the tree, nodded where it lay, and said to the barman: "There's the lassie's tree. Think much o't." He loosened his collar, ordered a large whisky—"An' A said whisky, Mick," he said—and glared at the four men seated round the fire.

"Whit's wrang, Harry?" Big Weellum asked him, while winking to Gallacher. "Ha'e ye seen a ghaist or something?"

Harry drained his dram, and asked for another. Gallacher nodded to Mick. "This one's on me," he said. Harry thanked the big farmer, threw back his head, drained his second dram, and began to feel better. He turned to stare at Big Weellum.

"Mebbe you'd like tae gang oot there yoursel' an' see whit A seen?" he taunted him.

"Whit did ye see, Soo-mooth?" Gallacher asked him, not mockingly. "Tell us."

Big Weellum laughed sarcastically. Gallacher frowned. Jock Simpson looked quizzically at the big roadman. The moocher said nothing; he listened. Though not superstitious himself, Pate had been out in the woods enough at night to know that a man could have queer thoughts. Harry, who had been determined to say nothing from the moment he set eyes on Big Weellum, now found the whisky loosening his tongue. He turned to Gallacher.

"A could tell ye," he said. "An' ha'e Weellum the cuddy laughin' at me. But A seen it jist the same!"

"Ach, ye ha'e been drinkin' bad whusky!" Big Weellum bantered. "Or maybe even monkey's bluid. Ye'll be tellin' us next ye saw Jean!"

"Pit a sock in it, Weellum!" Gallacher said quietly. "You're aye needlin'. Tell us, Soo-mooth," he finished. He called for another dram for Harry, and Harry, ignoring Big Weellum, addressed Jock and the farmer.

"A'm walkin' on the road," he began, "wi' a tree for Mick's lass. . . ." Harry always used the present tense when describing something that had involved himself. He went on:

"Well, A'm jist aboot at the pound when A sees this white thing wi' claes flappin' an' a'. A had a couple in Alec's, an' says A tae masel, says A: A'm seein' things. But A looks again, an' it's richt enough. She's there. . . ."

He tipped his glass and drained it.

"So A hurries on," he continued, "an' then, near the big quarry, A hears this clankin' soon', like metal it was. Then A seen thur green lichts—twa here, twa there, a' ower the place in fact. That was near the quarry. Weellum the cuddy wid ha'e gaed efter them tae see what they were but A jist hurried on here. There's things a body's better leavin' alane.

"Mebbe A imagined Jean," he said aggressively, "but A

didna dream up her dugs wi' the green een! Nor the horns," he added finally, "for A seen them tae!"

Big Weellum guffawed. He rocked on his seat and pounded the table with his enormous palm till he spilled his beer. His face turned as red as a turkey cock's. It was clear that Weellum was on to something that nobody else knew about.

"Soo-mooth!" he exploded at last. "Ye're the greatest haverer in the world. Ye could have bate wee Gobbles in a canter." Weellum had once attended lectures on Current Affairs run by the W.E.A. "Ye saw Jean a' right. I ken that because I built hersel' this morn'—built her wi' snaw an' dressed her in an auld curtain o' the wife's—but the bit ye added on tae the story . . . that was pure whusky an' Gobbles! I'll eat a' the ghosts on the mair! The joke's on you, so whit's aboot a bit sang?"

The others looked at Harry. Harry knew what they were thinking. If Jean was made of snow, and was there, manufactured by Big Weellum, they would be thinking he had invented the rest. Harry turned angrily to Weellum:

"Listen, fly man!" he began; "if ye think . . ." He stopped. He winked deliberately at Gallacher and Jock. Then: "Whit wid ye like me tae sing, Weellum?" he asked politely. "Maybe 'The Felons of our Land' or 'Stirlin' Brig' or your favourite 'Kevin Barry'?"

Big Weellum's lip tightened on the instant. Patriotic Scots or Irish songs made him furious, and he was never slow to show it. He was one of those Anglicised Scots who thought that 1690 and 1707 were the only dates that mattered, and on that theme he was humourless and beyond humouring. Gallacher saw the fire kindling, and eased himself to his feet to intervene, but before Weellum could think up a reply to Harry's thrust there was a loud knocking at the front door.

"Who's there?" Mick, the barman, shouted, and got his answer in a Highland voice: "It iss the polees. Open up!"

Mick opened the door and the wind almost swung it in his face. The village sergeant stalked ponderously into the room, stamping his feet and clapping his mittened hands.

"Well! Well!" he greeted them, drawing a chair up to the fire. "Here am I on my way home on this cold night, and

thinking there might be burglars in the place. You'll all be
Mick's guests I'm sure, being the time of night it is, so I'll haf
a haf on the house myself. But gif me it from under the counter
Mick!" he called to the barman; "it iss whisky I want, and
not the stuff you fill the paraffeen lamps with, whateffer!"

Mick brought the sergeant his whisky. "*Slainte!*" the
sergeant greeted them, and sipped. "I wass thinking when I
saw the lights on that there must be new licensing hours in the
village. . . ."

He drained his dram and tossed Mick a coin. "Bring me
another one Mick!" he ordered. "It iss a cold night and it will
help keep away the measles or whateffer it iss a man might
catch in this place of iniquity. But what iss wrong with Big
Weellum?" he asked.

"Oh, Harry here offered to sing him some sangs he didna
like," Gallacher told him. "But Harry has seen Jean, Tam.
Dugs an' a'!"

The sergeant looked at Harry speculatively. "If he wass
drinking Mick's whisky, I'm not surprised," he said. "Sometimes it makes me see things myself. Right now I am imagining
I see five men here drinking an hour and a half after shutting
time. Och, it would be a terrible thing if the polees were to
come in whateffer. . . ."

"Whit Harry saw was a snawman that Weellum built," Jock
interrupted him. "But Weellum didna make the dugs an' the
thing that rattled. Wis that bit true, Harry?" he asked.

"It was true, Jock," Haverin' Harry answered, then glared
at Weellum.

"Havers!" Big Weellum mocked him.

"Go tae hell!" said Harry with emphasis.

"Noo, listen, Soo-mooth!" Big Weellum flared at him,
jumping to his feet. "If ye think . . ."

"Now, now, my bodachs," the sergeant interrupted him.
"This iss a serious discussion on bogles and other mysterious
manifestations. And I haf the most beautiful cell down the
road doing nothing. . . ." The eyes that looked at Weellum
were humorous. "You don't haf to go to hell if you don't want
to go, Weellum." And Weellum sat down, chastened.

"Dammit, but there's wan way o' findin' oot aboot a' this,"

said Gallacher suddenly. "Whit aboot us a' gangin' doon the road an' seein' whit's tae be seen?"

"That's whit I was thinkin'," the moocher said, "so whit are we waitin' for?"

"Ballocks!" said Big Weellum.

"Och, well, now," the sergeant laughed, "it would take the argument out of the academic sphere, and it iss the silly season anyway. And you neffer can tell, to be sure. It iss only a few minutes to the quarry in the car."

The party, headed by the policeman, stalked from the lounge and waited while Mick locked up. "I'm for home myself," Mick said. "Youse can tell me all about the ghosts in the mornin'."

The moocher started up his little rabbit van and chugged slowly along the snow-bound road; the others climbed into Gallacher's car, with Jock taking the wheel. The wind was still blowing hard across the moor, but there was no powder-swirl of snow, and the sky was clear blue, with Orion glittering.

The cars made about eight miles an hour till the heaters cleared the ice from the windscreens; then they made fifteen, lurching, skidding and spinning on the frozen snow. The head-lamps picked out cat's eyes and rat eyes, and the eyes of Black-face hoggs down for wintering. And once a white owl flapped slowly through the beam.

After fifteen minutes, they were well across the moor, near the quarry, and Harry shouted to Jock to stop. Jock hooted to the moocher in front, and car and van drew in to the side of the road, near the first of the saugh bushes, which were snow-crusted and frosted.

The men piled out on to the road, breathing vapour and jigging with the cold. "We're daft!" grunted Big Weellum, turning up the collar of his jacket against the biting wind.

"We'll soon ken who's daft," the moocher said. "Let's take a gander an' see whit's whit." Slim, agile and light of foot, he leaped across the road-side ditch, and, presently, was shining his torch on the snow. Jock led the rest of the party across the ditch by an easier route, and in a moment they joined the moocher.

"You're share this is the place?" the moocher asked Haverin'
Harry. He was arcing his torch over the snow, searching with
shrewd, kenning eyes.

"Near enough," Harry told him. "There's the saugh bushes
ower there, and the noise wisna far frae here."

The sergeant was watching Pate with his torch. "Py chove,
Pate!" he said: "I'll bet this iss the first time you've had the
polees as company out here at this time of night. Now, iff you
wass to fall over a pheasant or something . . ." Pate grinned.

"Ony time he fa's ower a phaisant," Gallacher put in, "he
gets up wi' the bliddy thing in his pooch!" Pate grinned again,
but said nothing.

Presently, Jock went back to the car for another torch.
When he returned he spoke to the moocher, and they stepped
away twenty paces apart, shining their torches in front of them.
Gallacher and Haverin' Harry followed Jock; Big Weellum
and the sergeant went with Pate.

Suddenly the moocher was shouting: "Jock! Cummeer an'
ha'e a look at this!"

Jock came running across the snowed-up heather, followed
by Gallacher and Harry. He shone his torch on the ground and
burst out laughing.

"Fox tracks!" he said. "Man, Harry, it wid be a fox ye saw
wi' the een. An' efter seein' Jean I can see how ye thocht. . . ."

"But A seen lots o' een!" Harry said doggedly. "Fower here
an' fower there—a' ower the place they wur."

Without speaking, Jock and the moocher back-tracked along
the fox's line to the road, then searched along the top of the
ditch. They looked up the road, and down, from the point
where the tracks left the ditch, and within five minutes found
four other sets of neat prints, all converging on the scrub.
Between the third and fourth set of prints they found other
tracks which had not been made by foxes.

"Whit d'ye mak' o't, Jock?" asked the moocher.

"If we're seein' richt," said Jock, rubbing his hands against
the cold, "there's five foxes in a bunch like a bliddy wolf-pack,
unless the wan fox went back tae the road and crossed the
ditch tae the mair five times. That disna make sense. But it's
the ither tracks that're puzzlin' me!"

Gallacher leaned over Jock's shoulder to look at the tracks in the snow. "If there's five foxes on the loose they're bliddy substantial barghaists!" he said. "I never heard tell o' foxes packin' afore. Onyway, accordin' tae the foxhunter there's no supposed tae be five foxes left between here an' Mossrigg."

"Ho-ho!" the sergeant exclaimed. "I'm shure the wish would be the father of that thought. Now, up yonder where I come from—where the whisky is born and foxes are gey beasts—my brother who iss a keeper has seen four foxes feeding on a dead stag when the winter iss hard. Hunger iss a terrible thing whateffer!"

"Thur foxes don't hiv tae be *reely* thegither, Wull," Jock said to the farmer. "They micht jist a' be attracted by the same thing?"

"Aye, but what thing?" said Gallacher.

While this learned discussion was taking place the moocher was following the line of strange prints, kneeling every now and again to examine them closely. Presently he called to Jock:

"If I don't miss ma guess this is roe deer tracks, but they seem tae be scuffed at nearly every step wi' somethin' else—as if the beast had somethin' fankled on its leg mebbe. . . ."

Jock stared at him. "Pate!" he said, "mebbe you've hit it richt on the heid. Harry heard a noise like the clankin' o' metal he said. If the roe had been in a trap—it's happened afore—that micht be it. Man, man! Wid that no' be the best ghost story o' the year?"

"An' it must be it!" he exclaimed suddenly, "for Harry said he thocht he saw horns. Five foxes moochin' efter wan trapped roe! Weellum's gaun tae hiv some ghosts tae eat the nicht!"

"It'll no dae, Jock," the moocher broke in, "the bit aboot the horns I mean. It's nearly Christmas. Nae buck wid ha'e horns at this time o' year . . . or wid it?"

"It canny be onything else," Jock said. "It's late in the year richt enough, but the beast must jist be a late caster. It could happen."

"That'll be right, too," the sergeant put in. "My brother, the one who iss the keeper, hass seen a buck with antlers after Ne'erday, and he wass sober at the time." He turned and patted

Haverin' Harry on the back with mock ceremony. "So you wass right enough, Soo-mooth," he said. "Py chove, Weellum," he turned to Big Weellum, "it iss a good thing we can't catch Harry's ghosts or you'd be here all night with a knife and fork whateffer!"

"If the beasts a' went in the direction o' the quarry . . ." Pate was thinking aloud, and Jock at once saw his train of thought.

"Man, Pate, if they did. . . . Weellum micht get that ghost dinner yet! Let's tak a bit look an' see."

Big Weellum, not liking the way things were shaping, stalked away towards the cars, muttering ill-humoured comment about theories, and detectives and Red Indians. Jock spoke to the others.

"Look, Wull, Tam," he said to Gallacher and the sergeant, "you twa gang back tae the car wi' Harry here, an' Pate an' I'll gang tae the quarry an' see whit's whit. It's dangerous in this snaw!"

Gallacher agreed, though he was already satisfied about ghosts and devils. "But tak care!" he warned them, "nae ghost's worth a broken neck. . . ."

Jock and Pate plodded through the deep, squeaking snow towards the quarry, following the line of the roebuck from the bushes. The line took them right to the edge of the big whin-stone quarry. Three sets of fox tracks accompanied it all the way, right to the brink. And there all tracks disappeared.

The men looked to right and left. No track turned off. All disappeared; just where a great eave of snow, drifted on the brink by the wind, and frozen, had fallen away and crashed to the ground far below.

The searchers back-tracked from the edge of the quarry and high-stepped down the slope to the lorry road. As they tramped along it towards the crusher they saw two dark shapes drifting over the snow—two seeming wraiths in shape of dogs. Foxes!

"There go twa o' Jean's dugs, Pate," said Jock. They crossed the hutch road, and picked their way among great, snow-capped whin boulders to a spot below the brink from which the snow-eave had fallen. And they found there what they were now expecting to find—a dead roebuck, with long, smooth draidlets of antlers, lying among the rocks.

He was lying, broken, bloody and partly eaten, with a gin-trap fastened to a hindfoot. Nearby lay the bodies of three foxes, who had followed him to his death when the snow gave way beneath their feet, probably when they were leaping at him, trying to pull him down. He was a small beast, and emaciated, and there would be little fight left in him.

Jock grasped one of the buck's antlers and tugged. It was firmly anchored. He tried the other, which came away in his hand. He put it in his side pocket. "Harry was seein' things richt enough," he said to the moocher, "an' a' reel ghosts at that, Pate. Soo-mooth's no' sic a haverer efter a'!"

Pate, ever practical, and thinking of bounties, cut the brushes from all three foxes. "Thirty bob," he said, as he stuffed them in his poacher's pocket, "an' a' because Weellum made a snaw-man!"

And that is really all of it, except for the bad grace of Big Weellum when he realised that his ghost-building prank had misfired.

All the men were in the cars when Jock and Pate got back to the road. They told their story, and threw the fox brushes and the roe antler in Big Weellum's lap to convince him that every word Soo-mooth had said was true.

Jock climbed in to the wheel of Gallacher's car while Pate returned alone to his little van. Both cars picked slowly away on the frozen road.

They were just started when Harry turned to Weellum, who was hunched up in a corner of the back seat, in a great huff: "Noo that ye've seen ma ghosts, Weellum," he bantered, "A'll sing ye a bit sang." Weellum said nothing and Harry began:

> *In Mountjoy one Monday morning*
> *High upon the gallows tree*
> *Kevin Barry gave his . . .*

"Stop!" Weellum roared. "Stop this damned car an' let me oot! I'll gang wi' Pate. It's easy seen I'm no' wanted here!"

Gallacher nudged Jock, who stopped the car. Weellum scrambled out on to the snow-bound road and walked back towards the van, which had also stopped. "Pate," he said; then he stopped. In the van the moocher was singing:

> *To Scotia's ancient realm*
> *Proud Edward's armies came.*

Weellum strode right past the van with a scowl on his weather-beaten face. Both cars waited but he did not turn about. He was in his 1690/1707 huff. Gallacher wound down his window and called out to him:

"Mind the barghaists Weellum! An' if ye see Jean tell her we were askin' for her. . . ."

Jock and Pate let in their clutches, and Weellum was left to walk back to the village.